SPANISH GCSE

REVISION QUICKIES

ENVIRONMENT, HEALTH & CAREER

 THE LANGUAGE GYM

ACKNOWLEDGEMENTS

Our heartfelt thanks to our team of guest proofreaders: Aurélie Lethuilier, Nadim Cham, Jérôme Nogues, Ana del Casar, Chris Pye, Sonja Fedrizzi & Anneliese Davies. Their contributions have ensured not only a highly accurate book, but also helped make some improvements in terms of choice of lexis. Thank you for lending your time and expertise to this project.

Our gratitude to Martin Lapworth for his time spent creating online versions of the Sentence Builders books linked to the Revision Quickies series. These are now available, via subscription, on SentenceBuilders.com. Thank you.

Dylan would like to thank his eagle-eyed students, Nicole Sun, Natalie Wong, Shweta Nair, Joshua Tomson, Marc Tang, Sam Sajan, Zoe Skinner, Alba Confalone and Simran Kamal for their excellent feedback and contribution during the final testing phase of this book.

Lastly, thanks to all the wonderful, supportive and passionate educators on Twitter who have helped enhance our books with their suggestions and comments, and to the members of the Global Innovative Language Teachers (GILT) Facebook group for their engagement with the Sentence Builders series. We consider ourselves very lucky to have such colleagues to inspire and spur us on.

Imprint: Independently Published
Edited by Jaume Llorens, Inés Głowacka & Paloma Lozano García

 THE LANGUAGE GYM

ABOUT THIS BOOK

As the title clearly suggests, this resource is intended for GCSE exam revision with a focus on the consolidation of high-frequency and high-surrender-value words and lexical chunks. Since the content closely matches the vocabulary included in our Spanish GCSE Revision, "Environment, Health & Career" the two books should be used together for best results.

The design of the 'quickies' is based on the key principle that durable vocabulary learning is more likely to occur when lexical items are processed deeply, repeatedly and at every level of grain, i.e. meaning, syntax, lexicogrammar, orthography. Accordingly, each quickie recycles the key vocabulary several times over; builds word associations; elicits deeper level of cognitive investment on the part of the learners and includes tasks which involve semantic processing and others which involve a focus on collocations, colligations, grammar and spelling. In order to cater for differentiated learning, we have included two sets of quickies per unit: a foundation-level set and a higher-level set, the latter including more challenging vocabulary and tasks.

Each unit ends with a productive retrieval-practice assessment which may be used to test summatively the uptake of the vocabulary practiced in each unit or merely as an extra revision tool.

The revision quickie's format has been tried and tested for years, and is based on the huge success of Dr Gianfranco Conti's GCSE French and Spanish revision quickies, the most downloaded language learning resources of all times on www.tes.com.

We hope both you and your students find this book useful.

Gianfranco, Ronan & Dylan

TABLE OF CONTENTS

THE LANGUAGE GYM

Unit 1. Food and eating out

KEY VOCABULARY - Foundation

La comida (*food*)

El arroz: *Rice*

El azúcar: *Sugar*

El helado: *Ice cream*

El queso: *Cheese*

El jamón: *Ham*

El pan: *Bread*

El pescado: *Fish*

El pollo: *Chicken*

La carne: *Meat*

La comida frita: *Fried food*

La ensalada: *Salad*

La mermelada: *Jam*

La tarta: *Cake*

Las espinacas: *Spinach*

Las fresas: *Strawberries*

Las manzanas: *Apples*

Las patatas: *Potatoes*

Las patatas fritas: *Fries*

Las setas: *Mushrooms*

Las verduras: *Vegetables*

Los dulces: *Sweets*

Los huevos: *Eggs*

Los mariscos: *Seafood*

Los pasteles: *Pastries*

Las bebidas (*drinks*)

El agua (mineral): *(Mineral) water*

El vino blanco: *White wine*

El vino tinto: *Red wine*

El zumo de fruta: *Fruit juice*

La cerveza: *Beer*

Los refrescos: *Fizzy drinks*

Key verbs

Beber: *To drink* / Comer: *To eat*

Gustar: *To like*

Pedir: *To order*

Querer: *To want*

Tomar: *To have*

Key phrases

Me apetece: *I fancy*

Me encanta: *I love*

Me gusta (mucho): *I like (a lot)*

Me gustaría: *I would like*

No me gusta: *I don't like*

No soporto: *I can't stand*

Quiero: *I want*

1. Gapped translation

a. Me gusta la carne: *I like* _____

b. No quiero patatas fritas: *I* _____ _____ *any fries*

c. Me encanta el pescado: *I love* _____

d. No como mariscos: *I don't eat* _____

e. Me gustan mucho las fresas: *I like* _____ *a lot*

f. No me gusta el azúcar: *I don't like* _____

g. Como ensalada: *I eat* _____

h. Me encantan las patatas: *I love* _____

i. No como pasteles: *I don't eat* _____

2. Complete the table

English	Español
Pastries	
	Me gustan los mariscos
Ice cream	
	Me encantan las verduras
	Odio los huevos
Sweets	
	No como carne
Fried food	

3. Categories – Sort the words below in the appropriate category

a. Una tarta b. Espinacas c. Manzanas d. Patatas
e. Vino tinto f. Setas g. Fresas h. Dulces i. Agua
j. Zumo de fruta k. Pasteles

Frutas	Verduras	Dulces	Bebidas

4. Faulty translation – Be careful, some are correct!

a. No soporto: *I don't like*

b. No como dulces: *I don't eat fried food*

c. No bebo vino blanco: *I don't drink red wine*

d. Me encantan las patatas: *I love apples*

e. Bebo mucha agua: *I drink a lot of water*

f. Nunca como pasteles: *I never eat pasta*

g. No quiero azúcar: *I don't want sugar*

h. Quiero unas fresas: *I want some apples*

5. Match

Pasteles	*Apple juice*
Verduras	*Pasta*
Beber	*Cakes*
Patatas	*To like*
Tartas	*Meat*
Pescado	*Potatoes*
Carne	*Fish*
Gustar	*Water*
Pasta	*Wine*
Vino	*Vegetables*
Agua	*Pastries*
Zumo de manzana	*To drink*

6. Broken words

a. Me gusta la car_ _ : *I like meat*

b. No como verd_ _ _ _ :
I don't eat vegetables

c. No soporto las espin_ _ _ _ :
I can't stand spinach

d. Quiero zu_ _ de manzana:
I would like some apple juice

e. No me apetece una cerv_ _ _ :
I don't fancy a beer

f. Tomo vino tin_ _ :
I have red wine

g. No como dul_ _ _:
I don't eat sweets

h. Siempre tomo comida fr_ _ _ :
I always have fried food

7. Translate into English

a. No tomo verduras

b. No soporto las espinacas

c. Me encanta el pescado

d. Me gusta mucho la pasta

e. No como pescado

f. A menudo como mariscos

g. No bebo vino ni cerveza

h. Para el almuerzo tomo una ensalada

i. Para la cena como pollo

8. Sentence puzzle

a. padres Mis comen carne mucha:
My parents eat a lot of meat

b. Me beber agua gustaría: *I would like to drink water*

c. el desayuno Para huevos tomo:
For breakfast, I have eggs

d. Me un refresco beber gustaría
I would like to drink a soft drink

e. No verduras como: *I don't eat vegetables*

f. cerveza No bebo: *I don't drink beer*

g. Me de manzana un zumo gustaría:
I would like an apple juice

9. Complete with the missing endings

a. Me apetec__ comer carn__

b. Quier__ beber agu__

c. Para el desayun__ tomo cereales con lech__

d. No com__ verdura__ mu_ a menud_

e. Mis padre__ comen muchos dulce__

f. ¿Quieres beber vin__ blanc__?

g. No beb__ cervez__

h. Me gustarí__ un zumo de naranj__

10. Word-level translation into Spanish

a. *Eggs*:   g. *To like*:

b. *Spinach*:   h. *To drink*:

c. *Vegetables*:   i. *To eat*:

d. *Sweets*:   j. *I can't stand*:

e. *Water*:   k. *I don't eat*:

f. *Fried food*:   l. *I want*:

11. Sentence-level translation into Spanish

a. I can't stand spinach. I prefer mushrooms.

b. I like pasta a lot. I also like bread and rice.

c. I would like an apple juice.

d. I can't stand vegetables but I eat a lot of fruit.

e. I want sweets this evening.

f. For dinner, I usually have fish and potatoes.

g. For breakfast, I usually have eggs with ham.

h. For lunch, I usually have meat and vegetables or fries.

i. I don't like meat but I love fish and seafood.

KEY VOCABULARY - Higher

Las comidas *(meals)*

Para el almuerzo, como: *For lunch, I eat*

Para el desayuno tomo: *For breakfast, I have*

Para la merienda, bebo: *For snack, I drink*

Para la cena, tomo: *For dinner, I have*

La comida *(food)* **y las bebidas** *(drinks)*

El agua: *Water*

El cerdo: *Pork* / El pollo: *Chicken*

La carne de ternera: *Beef*

La comida frita: *Fried food*

Las gambas: *Prawns*

Los mariscos: *Seafood*

Los refrescos: *Fizzy drinks*

Adjectives to describe food

Bueno/a: *Good*

Delicioso/a: *Delicious*

Dulce: *Sweet*

Grasiento/a: *Greasy*

Nutritivo/a: *Nutritious*

Picante: *Spicy*

Soso/a: *Bland*

Salado/a: *Salty*

Saludable: *Healthy*

Sabroso/a: *Tasty*

Suculento: *Succulent*

Intensifiers

Bastante: *Quite*

Demasiado: *Too*

Muy: *Very*

Realmente: *Really*

Un poco: *A bit*

Saying what I want to order

Quiero pedir: *I want to order*

Me gustaría beber: *I would like to drink*

Nos gustaría comer: *We would like to eat*

Saying what I like/dislike

Lo que me gusta comer: *What I like eating*

Lo que menos me gusta: *What I like the least*

Lo que más me gusta: *What I like the most*

Lo que no soporto: *What I can't stand*

Lo que odio: *What I hate*

Lo que odio comer: *What I hate eating*

Mi comida favorita es: *My favourite food is*

Mi plato favorito es: *My favourite dish is*

1. Match

La comida	*Seafood*
Los mariscos	*Snack*
El almuerzo	*To drink*
Pedir	*Good*
La carne de ternera	*Greasy*
Picante	*Beef*
Las gambas	*Sugar*
Bueno	*Prawns*
Azúcar	*Lunch*
Grasiento	*Food*
Beber	*To order*
La merienda	*Spicy*

2. Gapped translation

a. Nos gustaría _____ agua:
We would like to order water

b. Me gustaría _____ una hamburguesa:
I would like to have a burger

c. Para el_____, tomo _____ caliente:
For breakfast, I have some hot chocolate

d. Lo que _____ me gusta es el _____:
What I like the least is cheese

e. Lo que _____, son las _____:
What I hate are vegetables

f. Lo que más me _____ , son las _____:
What I like the most are prawns

g. Me gustaría comer _____ de ternera:
I would like to eat beef

h. Lo que no _____ es la _____ frita:
What I can't stand is fried food

3. Missing letters

a. de__si__o : *too*

b. p__i_ : *to order*

c. u_ p__o : *a bit*

d. s_b_o_o : *tasty*

e. b__e_ : *to drink*

f. s_l_d__l_ : *healthy*

g. r__lm_n__ : *really*

h. c_m__a : *food*

i. g__b_s : *prawns*

j. _u__e_ : *sweets*

4. Broken words

a. Gam_____ : *prawns*

b. Pic_____ : *spicy*

c. Demasi___ : *too*

d. Du_____ : *sweet*

e. Real_____ : *really*

f. Beb___ : *to drink*

g. Sabr_____ : *tasty*

h. Com_____: *food*

i. Com_____ : *to eat*

j. Salu_____ : *healthy*

5. Spot and fix the incorrect translations – PLEASE NOTE: not all the sentences contain mistakes!

a. Mi comida favorita: *My favourite drink*

b. Lo que no soporto: *What I can't stand*

c. Me gusta la comida picante: *I love spicy food*

d. Para la merienda, tomo: *For dinner, I have*

e. Es bastante saludable: *It's quite healthy*

f. Es demasiado salado: *It's too bland*

g. Nos gustaría pedir: *We would like to order*

h. Quiero comprar: *You would like to buy*

i. Lo que menos me gusta: *What I like the most*

j. Mi plato favorito: *My favourite snack*

k. Es realmente sabroso: *It's really bad*

l. La carne es deliciosa: *The meat is disgusting*

6. Anagrams

a. Cmioda:

b. Meradien:

c. liciDeoso:

d. Reantelme:

e. Pired:

f. Pitecan:

g. Patol:

h. osoabSr:

7. Sentence puzzle

a. la comida Me encanta picante:

b. Lo me gusta es la que más carne:

c. es La sabrosa paella muy:

d. pedir gustaría un Me café:

e. Me los mariscos encantan:

f. La rica en ternera proteínas es de carne:

g. bocadillo almuerzo tomo Para el un:

h. Lo verduras soporto son que no las:

8. Complete the table

English	Español
What I like the least	
	La comida picante
	La comida dulce
We would like	
	Pedir agua
I have seafood	
	Lo que más me gusta
It is too salty	
It is very healthy	

9. Wordsearch: Find the Spanish for the listed words

R	O	M	S	T	E	O	Z
E	T	N	A	C	I	P	N
A	A	I	B	L	H	E	Y
L	L	C	R	S	O	L	A
M	P	N	O	L	E	B	T
E	C	J	S	M	L	A	E
N	R	R	O	A	B	D	W
T	A	E	T	L	I	U	H
E	M	B	A	C	S	L	S
B	U	E	N	O	R	A	I
L	Y	B	O	S	O	S	M
E	I	L	A	T	A	N	R
O	N	I	Ü	G	N	I	P

Good: B

Healthy: S

Really: R

Spicy: P

Very: M

Tasty: S

To drink: B

Bland: S

Dish: P

Bad: M

10. Guided translation

a. *Fizzy drinks*: L___ r_____

b. *Too salty*: D_____ s_____

c. *For lunch*: P____ e_ a_____

d. *Really good*: R_____ b_____

e. *Very healthy*: M____ s_____

f. *We would like*: N____ g_____

g. *For snack*: P___ l_ m_____

h. *What I can't stand*: L__ q__ n__ s_____

i. *It's bland*: E__ s_____

j. *Spicy food*: L__ c_____ p_____

k. *I would like*: M__ g_____

11. Translate into Spanish

a. For breakfast, I have some eggs and a bit of fruit.

b. For lunch, I eat fish and vegetables.

c. For snack, I have a cheese sandwich and a coffee.

d. What I can't stand are fizzy drinks and French fries.

e. I don't like burgers because they are too greasy.

f. What I love is fried food, but it's not healthy.

g. What I like the most is beef because it's tasty.

h. What I like the least are prawns and vegetables.

i. I would like to eat seafood and drink water.

j. I love spicy and salty food. I don't like sweet food.

 THE LANGUAGE GYM

UNIT 1 Test (/100)

1. Vocabulary recognition – Spanish to English gapped translation (/15)

a. Mi plato favorito es la carne de ternera en salsa: *My favourite _____ is _____ in sauce*

b. Lo que más me gusta es el pollo: _____ *I like _____, is _____*

c. Para el almuerzo, no como carne: *For _____ I don't _____ any _____*

d. Me encantan los mariscos pero no me gusta el pescado: *I love _____ but I don't like _____*

e. Me gustaría pedir vino y queso: *I _____ to _____ some wine and _____*

f. Nos gustaría comer verduras esta noche: *We would like to eat some _____ this _____*

2. Syntax/Lexicogrammar – Split sentences (/5)

Lo que mas me gusta son	**comemos una ensalada o un trozo de queso**
Para el desayuno, por lo general tomo	**asado con patatas**
Mi plato favorito es	**los mariscos**
Por la tarde no comemos mucho. Nosotros	**una tostada con miel**
Me gustaría pedir pollo	**la paella y la ensalada verde**

3. Grammar/Morphology/Vocabulary – Tangled translation (/20)

a. Me gustaría comer **bread** para el **breakfast**

b. **That which** no soporto, son las **prawns**

c. Mi **food favourite**, es el pescado

d. Esta **meat** es realmente **good**

e. Para el desayuno, nosotros **have eggs**

f. Ayer **I drunk water** mineral

g. Para el desayuno, **we drink tea**

h. Lo que más **I like** es el **rice**

i. **This** mañana, **I ate** una tostada

j. Para la **dinner**, nosotros **eat** verduras

4. Translate into Spanish (/ 60 – each full sentence = 6 points)

a. What I like the most is cheese.

b. For dinner, we eat meat or fish.

c. What I can't stand are vegetables.

d. I would like to buy meat for my lunch.

e. I love cheese because it's tasty.

f. Honey is very sweet and quite healthy.

g. What I can't stand is greasy food.

h. The chicken is delicious but the rice is bland.

i. I always eat eggs because they are nutritious.

j. I don't eat sugar because it isn't healthy.

Unit 1. Food and eating out - Foundation

1. Gapped translation
a. *I like* **meat**   b. *I* **don't want** *any fries*   c. *I love* **fish**   d. *I don't eat* **seafood**   e. *I like* **strawberries** *a lot*
f. *I don't like* **sugar**   g. *I eat* **salad**   h. *I love* **potatoes**   i. *I don't eat* **pastries/cakes**

2. Complete the table
Pastries: **Pasteles**   *I like seafood:* **Me gustan los mariscos**   *Ice cream:* **Helado**
I love vegetables: **Me encantan las verduras**   *I hate eggs:* **Odio los huevos**   *Sweets:* **Dulces/Caramelos**
I don't eat meat: **No como carne**   *Fried food:* **La comida frita**

3. Categories
Frutas: **Manzanas / Fresas**   Verduras: **Espinacas / Patatas / Setas**
Dulces: **Una tarta / Dulces / Pasteles**   Bebidas: **Vino tino / Agua / Zumo de fruta**

4. Faulty translation
a. No soporto: *I can't stand*   b. No como dulces: *I don't eat* **sweets**
c. No bebo vino blanco: *I don't drink* **white** *wine*   d. Me encantan las patatas: *I love* **potatoes**
e. Bebo mucha agua: *I drink a lot of water* √   f. Nunca como pasteles: *I never eat* **pastries**
g. No quiero azúcar: *I don't want sugar* √   h. Quiero unas fresas: *I want some* **strawberries**

5. Match
Pasteles – *Pastries*   Verduras – *Vegetables*   Beber – *To drink*   Patatas – *Potatoes*
Tartas – *Cakes*   Pescado – *Fish*   Carne – *Meat*   Gustar – *To like*   Pasta – *Pasta*
Vino – *Wine*   Agua – *Water*   Zumo de manzana – *Apple juice*

6. Broken words
a. Me gusta la car**ne**   b. No como verd**uras**   c. No soporta las espin**acas**   d. Quiero zu**mo** de manzana
e. No me apetece una cer**veza**   f. Tomo vino tin**to**   g. No como dul**ces**   h. Siempre tomo comida fr**ita**

7. Translate into English
a. I don't have vegetables   b. I can't stand spinach   c. I love fish   d. I like pasta a lot
e. I don't eat fish   f. I often eat seafood   g. I don't drink wine nor beer   h. For lunch I have a salad
i. At dinner I eat chicken

8. Sentence puzzle
a. Mis padres comen mucha carne   b. Me gustaría beber agua   c. Para el desayuno tomo huevos
d. Me gustaría beber un refresco   e. No como verduras   f. No bebo cerveza
g. Me gustaría un zumo de manzana

9. Complete with the missing endings
a. Me apetec**e** comer carne   b. Quier**o** beber agu**a**   c. Para el desayun**o** tomo cereales con lech**e**
d. No com**o** verdura**s** mu**y** a menud**o**   e. Mis padre**s** comen muchos dulce**s**   f. ¿Quieres beber vin**o** blanc**o**?
g. No beb**o** cervez**a**   h. Me gustarí**a** un zumo de naranj**a**

10. Word-level translation into Spanish
a. *Eggs:* **Huevos**   b. *Spinach:* **Espinacas**   c. *Vegetables:* **Verduras**   d. *Sweets:* **Dulces**   e. *Water:* **Agua**
f. *Fried food:* **Comida frita**   g. *To like:* **Gustar**   h. *To drink:* **Beber**   i. *To eat:* **Comer**
j. *I can't stand:* **No soporto**   k. *I don't eat:* **No como**   l. *I want:* **Quiero**

11. Sentence-level translation into Spanish
a. No soporto las espinacas. Prefiero las setas/los champiñones.   b. Me gusta mucho la pasta. También me gusta
el pan y el arroz.   c. Me gustaría un zumo de manzana.   d. No soporto las verduras pero como mucha fruta.
e. Quiero dulces esta tarde/noche.   f. Para la cena *normalmente como/tomo pescado y patatas.
g. Para el desayuno normalmente como/tomo huevos con jamón.   h. Para el almuerzo, normalmente como/tomo
carne y verduras o patatas fritas.   i. No me gusta la carne pero me encanta el pescado y el marisco.

*Allow "suelo comer/tomar"

Unit 1. Food and eating out - Higher

1. Match

La comida – **Food**   Los mariscos – **Seafood**   El almuerzo – **Lunch**   Pedir – **To order**
La carne de ternera – **Beef**   Picante – **Spicy**   Las gambas – **Prawns**   Bueno – **Good**   Azúcar – **Sugar**
Grasiento – **Greasy**   Beber – **To drink**   La merienda – **Snack**

2. Gapped translation

a. pedir   b. tomar   c. desayuno/chocolate   d. menos/queso   e. odio/verduras   f. gustan/gambas
g. un poco   h. no soporto, comida

3. Missing letters

a. **demasiado**: *too*   b. **pedir**: *to order*   c. **un poco**: *a bit*   d. **sabroso**: *tasty*   e. **beber**: *to drink*
f. **saludable**: *healthy*   g. **realmente**: *really*   h. **comida**: *food*   i. **gambas**: *prawns*   j. **dulces**: *sweets*

4. Broken words

a. Gam**bas**: *prawns*   b. Pic**ante**: *spicy*   c. Demasi**ado**: *too*   d. Dul**ce**: *sweet*   e. Real**mente**: *really*
f. Beb**er**: *to drink*   g. Sab**roso**: *tasty*   h. Com**ida**: *food*   i. Com**er**: *to eat*   j. Salu**dable**: *healthy*

5. Spot and fix the incorrect translations

a. Mi comida favorita: *My favourite **food***   g. Nos gustaría pedir: *We would like to order* √
b. Lo que no soporto: *What I can't stand* √   h. Quiero comprar: *I want to buy*
c. Me gusta la comida picante: *I **like** spicy food*   i. Lo que menos me gusta: *What I like the **least***
d. Para la merienda, tomo: *For **snack**, I have*   j. Mi plato favorito: *My favourite **dish***
e. Es bastante saludable: *It's quite healthy* √   k. Es realmente sabroso: *It's really **tasty***
f. Es demasiado salado: *It's too **salty***   l. La carne es deliciosa: *The meat is **delicious***

6. Anagrams

a. Comida   b. Merienda   c. Delicioso   d. Realmente   e. Pedir   f. Picante   g. Plato   h. Sabroso

7. Sentence puzzle

a. Me encanta la comida picante   b. Lo que más me gusta es la carne   c. La paella es muy sabrosa
d. Me gustaría pedir un café   e. Me encantan los mariscos   f. La carne de ternera es rica en proteínas
g. Para el almuerzo tomo un bocadillo   h. Lo que no soporto son las verduras

8. Complete the table

What I like the least: **Lo que menos me gusta**   *Spicy food:* **La comida picante**   *Sweet food:* **La comida dulce**
We would like: **Nos gustaría**   *To order water:* **Pedir agua**   *I have seafood:* **Tomo mariscos**
What I like the most: **Lo que más me gusta**   *It is too salty:* **Es demasiado salado**
It is very healthy: **Es muy saludable**

9. Wordsearch

R	O	M	S				
E	T	N	A	C	I	P	
A	A		B	L		E	
L	L		R		O	L	
M	P		O			B	
E			S			A	
N		R	O			D	
T		E				U	
E	M	B				L	
B	U	E	N	O		A	
	Y	B	O	S	O	S	

Good:	**Bueno**
Healthy:	**Saludable**
Really:	**Realmente**
Spicy:	**Picante**
Very:	**Muy**
Tasty:	**Sabroso**
To drink:	**Beber**
Bland:	**Soso**
Dish:	**Plato**
Bad:	**Malo**

10. Guided translation

a. **Los refrescos** b. **Demasiado salado/a**
c. **Para el almuerzo** d. **Realmente bueno**
e. **Muy saludable** f. **Nos gustaría**
g. **Para la merienda** h. **Lo que no soporto**
i. **Es soso** j. **La comida picante**
k. **Me gustaría**

11. Translate into Spanish

a. Para el desayuno, tomo unos huevos y un poco de fruta.   b. Para el almuerzo, como pescado y verduras.
c. Para la merienda, tomo un bocadillo de queso y un café.   d. Lo que no soporto son los refrescos y las patatas
fritas.   e. No me gustan las hamburguesas porque son demasiado grasientas.   f. Lo que me encanta es la comida
frita, pero no es saludable.   g. Lo que más me gusta es la carne de ternera porque es sabrosa.
h. Lo que menos me gustan son las gambas y las verduras.   i. Me gustaría comer mariscos y beber agua.
j. Me encanta la comida picante y salada. No me gusta la comida dulce.

THE LANGUAGE GYM

ANSWERS – UNIT 1 – Test (/100)

1. Vocabulary recognition – Spanish to English gapped translation (/15)

a. Mi plato favorito es la carne de ternera en salsa: *My favourite **dish** is **beef** in sauce*

b. Lo que más me gusta es el pollo: ***What** I like **most**, is **chicken***

c. Para el almuerzo, no como carne: *For **lunch** I don't **eat** any **meat***

d. Me encantan los mariscos pero no me gusta el pescado: *I love **seafood** but I don't like **fish***

e. Me gustaría pedir vino y queso: *I **would like** to **order** some wine and **cheese***

f. Nos gustaría comer verduras esta noche: *We would like to eat some **vegetables** this **evening***

2. Syntax/Lexicogrammar – Split sentences (/5)

Lo que más me gusta son	**los mariscos**
Para el desayuno, por lo general tomo	**una tostada con miel**
Mi plato favorito es	**la paella y la ensalada verde**
Por la tarde no comemos mucho. Nosotros	**comemos una ensalada o un trozo de queso**
Me gustaría pedir pollo	**asado con patatas**

3. Grammar/Morphology/Vocabulary – Tangled translation (/20)

a. Me gustaría comer **pan** para el **desayuno (2)**

b. **Lo que** no soporto, son las **gambas (2)**

c. Mi **comida favorita**, es el pescado **(2)**

d. Esta **carne** es realmente **buena (2)**

e. Para el desayuno, nosotros **tomamos huevos (2)**

f. Ayer **bebí agua** mineral **(2)**

g. Para el desayuno, **bebemos té (2)**

h. Lo que más **me gusta** es el **arroz (2)**

i. **Esta** mañana, **comí** una tostada **(2)**

j. Para la **cena**, nosotros **comemos** verduras **(2)**

4. Translate into Spanish (/ 60 – each full sentence – 6 points)

a. Lo que más me gusta, es el queso.

b. Para la cena, comemos carne o pescado.

c. Lo que no soporto son las verduras.

d. Me gustaría comprar carne para mi almuerzo.

e. Me encanta el queso porque es sabroso.

f. La miel es bastante dulce y bastante saludable.

g. Lo que no soporto es la comida grasienta.

h. El pollo es delicioso, pero el arroz es soso.

i. Siempre como huevos porque son nutritivos.

j. No como azúcar porque no es saludable.

 **THE LANGUAGE GYM**

Unit 2. Healthy/unhealthy living

KEY VOCABULARY - Foundation

1. Las buenas costumbres *(good habits)*

Como cinco porciones de frutas y verduras al día: *I eat five portions of fruit and vegetables per day*

Duermo ocho horas por noche:
I sleep eight hours per night

Evito la comida frita: *I avoid fried foods*

Hago ejercicio regularmente:
I exercise regularly

Me relajo: *I relax*

No como demasiada grasa:
I don't eat too much fat

No paso demasiado tiempo en mi ordenador/móvil:
I don't spend too much time on my computer/mobile

No tomo drogas:
I don't take any drugs

Salgo con mis amigos:
I go out with my friends

Sigo una dieta saludable:
I follow a healthy diet

2. Los malos hábitos *(bad habits)*

Bebo mucho alcohol:
I drink a lot of alcohol

Bebo muchos refrescos:
I drink a lot of fizzy drinks

Como muchos caramelos:
I eat a lot of sweets

Duermo lo suficiente: *I sleep enough*

Fumo: *I smoke*

No hago deporte: *I don't do sport*

Paso horas en la Play:
I spend hours on my PlayStation

Paso demasiado tiempo en las redes sociales:
I spend too much time on social media

Siempre estoy estresado/a:
I am always stressed

Tomo drogas: *I take drugs*

3. Los adjetivos útiles *(useful)*

Bueno/a: *Good*

Cansado/a: *Tired*

Dulce: *Sweet*

Equilibrado/a: *Balanced*

Grasiento/a: *Greasy*

Malo/a: *Bad*

Nocivo/a: *Harmful*

Peligroso/a: *Dangerous*

Saludable: *Healthy*

No es sano/a: *It is unhealthy*

1. Match (section 1)

Duermo	*I avoid*
Evito	*I go out*
No como	*Fried food*
La comida frita	*I sleep*
Me relajo	*A diet*
Grasa	*I relax*
En mi ordenador	*I don't eat*
Salgo	*On my computer*
Hago ejercicio	*Fat*
Una dieta	*I exercise*

2. Gapped translation (section 1)

a. Evito la comida frita: *I avoid _____*

b. No como demasiada grasa:
I don't eat too much _____

c. Sigo una dieta saludable:
I follow a _____ diet

d. Como cinco porciones de frutas y verduras al día:
I eat five portions of fruit and _____ per day

e. Hago ejercicio: *I _____*

f. Me relajo después del cole: *I _____ after school*

g. No tomo drogas: *I don't take _____*

3. Complete the sentences with a suitable verb and translate them into English (section 2)

a. Yo no _____ mucho alcohol

b. Yo siempre _____ estresado/a

c. Yo _____ muchos dulces

d. Yo _____ muchos cigarrillos

e. Yo _____ mucho tiempo en las redes sociales

f. Yo _____ mucha Coca Cola

4. Tick every sentence which refers to a healthy habit

a. Bebo mucho alcohol

b. Como cinco porciones de verduras al día

c. Paso ocho horas al día en mi ordenador

d. Paso muchas horas en las redes sociales

e. Como mucha comida frita y dulces

f. Evito la comida frita

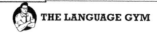

5. Complete the table (section 1)

English	Español
I sleep eight hours each night	
	Me relajo
	No como demasiada grasa
I follow a healthy diet	
	Salgo con mis amigos
I don't take drugs	
I exercise regularly	
	Evito la comida frita

6. Broken words (section 3)

a. Sa__dable: *Healthy*

b. No es s___: *It is not healthy*

c. B__no: *Good*

d. No___o: *Harmful*

e. Pel_____: *Dangerous*

f. ___ce: *Sweet*

g. Ma__: *Bad*

h. E___librado: *Balanced*

i.____ado: *Tired*

j. Gr____nto: *Greasy*

7. Gapped English to Spanish translation

a. *I sleep eight hours per night*: _____ ocho horas por _____

b. *I don't smoke cigarettes*: No_____ cigarrillos

c. *I avoid fried food*: Evito la _____ _____

d. *I spend hours on social media*: _____ horas en las _____ ____

e. *I exercise regularly*: Hago _____ frecuentemente

f. *Fried food is not healthy*: La comida frita no es _____

g. *I eat five portions of vegetables*: Como cinco porciones de _____

h. *I go out with my friends*: _____ con mis _____

i. *I don't drink a lot of alcohol*: No _____ mucho _____

j. *I don't sleep enough*: No _____ lo suficiente

8. Write the one word missing in each sentence

a. Yo ocho horas cada noche

b. No cigarrillos porque es malo para la salud

c. La comida frita mala para la salud

d. Paso mucho tiempo en las sociales

e. Yo una dieta muy sana

f. Normalmente no mucho azúcar

g. Siempre salgo mis amigos el fin de semana

9. Guided translation

a. Good: B____   f. Sweet: D____

b. Bad: M___   g. Tired: C_____

c. Health: S____   h. Drugs: D_____

d. Diet: D____   i. Time: T_____

e. Harmful: N____   j. Healthy: S_____

10. Translate into Spanish

a. I sleep at least eight hours each night

b. I am always tired and stressed

c. I don't smoke cigarettes

d. I avoid fried food and sweets

e. I spend a lot of time on social media and on my mobile phone

f. I follow a healthy diet

g. I exercise regularly, but I eat a lot of sweets

h. I don't take any drugs, but I smoke sometimes

i. I eat five portions of fruit and vegetables per day

j. I don't drink fizzy drinks

k. French fries are unhealthy because they are greasy

l. I spend one hour a day on the internet

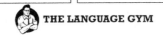 THE LANGUAGE GYM

KEY VOCABULARY - Higher

Qué hago para mantenerme en forma
(What I do to stay in shape)

Es necesario: *It is necessary to*

Intento: *I try to*

-beber mucha agua: *drink a lot of water*

-comer de forma saludable: *eat healthily*

-comer mucha fruta: *eat a lot of fruit*

-comer muchas verduras: *eat a lot of vegetables*

-descansar lo suficiente: *have enough rest*

-dormir 8 horas cada noche: *sleep 8 hours a night*

-hacer ejercicio regularmente: *exercise regularly*

-no fumar: *avoid smoking*

Qué como *(What I eat)*

Yo como: *I eat*

-comida sana: *healthy food*

-espinacas: *spinach*

-frutos secos: *nuts*

-huevos: *eggs*

-judías verdes: *green beans*

Las bebidas que bebo *(Drinks I drink)*

Yo bebo: *I drink*

-agua: *water*

-zumo de naranja: *orange juice*

-zumo de frutas: *fruit juice*

Expresiones de tiempo *(Time)*

Normalmente: *Usually* / En general: *In general*

Todos los días: *Every day*

Lo que debo hacer *(What I must do)*

Para mantenerme en forma: *To stay in shape*

Para mejorar mi salud: *To improve my health*

Para tener buena salud: *To be in good health*

Para tener energía: *To have energy*

Mis propósitos para el futuro

En el futuro, tengo la intención de:

In the future, I intend to

-dejar de beber alcohol: *stop drinking alcohol*

-dejar de fumar: *stop smoking*

Haré un esfuerzo para:

I'm going to make an effort to

-comer menos alimentos azucarados/grasos:
eat less sugary/fatty foods

-comer más verduras: *eat more vegetables*

Si pudiera... *(If I could...)*

-cocinaría más yo mismo/yo misma:
I would cook more myself

1. Match

Dormir	*To rest*
Evitar	*To stay in shape*
Fumar	*To smoke*
Mejorar	*To sleep*
Descansar	*To improve*
Dejar de fumar	*To make an effort*
Hacer un esfuerzo	*To cook*
Cocinar	*To stop smoking*
Mantenerme en forma	*To avoid*

2. Gapped translation

a. Bebo bastante agua: *I drink enough* _____

b. Como frutos secos: *I eat* _____

c. Para mantenerme en forma: *To stay in*_____

d. Buena salud: *Good* _____

e. Dejar de fumar: *To stop* _____

f. Como huevos: *I eat* _____

g. Me encantan las judías verdes: *I love* _____

h. Me encantan las espinacas: *I like* _____

3. Broken words

a. Salu_ _ _ _ _   g. Dor_ _ _

b. Alc_ _ _ _   h. Hue_ _ _

c. Du_ _ _ _   i. Espin_ _ _ _

d. Verd_ _ _ _   j. Fr_ _ _ _ s_ _ _ _

e. Norm_ _ _ _ _ _ _   k. Ag_ _

f. En el f_ _ _ _ _   l. Fum_ _

4. Complete with a suitable word

a. _____ zumo de naranja

b. Para mantenerme ___ forma

c. Todos ___ días bebo dos litros de agua

d. Tengo ___ intención de dejar de beber alcohol

e. Es necesario _____ lo suficiente

f. Como alimentos _____

g. Es necesario dormir ocho horas _____ noche

h. Para tener _____ salud

THE LANGUAGE GYM

5. Translate into English

a. Las espinacas:

b. Los dulces:

c. Si pudiera:

d. Salud:

e. Yo mismo:

f. Los huevos:

g. El agua:

h. Las verduras:

i. Fumar:

j. Alimentos sanos:

k. Yo cocinaría:

l. Tengo la intención de:

6. Missing vowels

a. L_s d_lc_s: *Sweets*

b. _s n_c_s r__: *It's necessary*

c. S_ p_d__r: *If I could*

d. M_n_s: *Less*

e. F_m_r: *To smoke*

f. _n _l f_t_r_: *In the future*

7. Anagrams

a. lcDesu

b. acaEsnspi

c. Farum

d. Dirmor

e. osneM

f. canDessar

g. Sudal

8. Sentence puzzle

a. Para descansar sano, es mantenerse necesario lo suficiente

b. Si cocinaría pudiera, yo mismo más

c. como mucha días Todos los fruta y verdura

d. En el fumar tengo dejar de futuro la intención de

e. en forma Como alimentos para mantenerme sanos

f. zumo de Normalmente bebo naranja

9. Complete the table

English	Español
Spinach	
	Si pudiera
To stop	
	Descansar
To smoke	
	Buena salud
To improve	
	Alimentos grasos
To stay in shape	

10. Wordsearch: Find the Spanish for the listed words

E	R	Z	U	M	O	E
S	I	N	A	O	N	A
P	S	M	G	N	E	D
I	A	E	Ü	I	U	R
N	R	N	R	L	B	E
A	E	O	A	P	D	Y
C	R	S	E	R	P	A
A	G	U	A	N	R
S	Z	J	N	M	E	N
N	E	M	A	U	C	B
D	A	R	E	F	I	A

To be: S

Good: B

Less: M

To stop: D

To smoke: F

Health: S

Spinach: E

Water: A

Juice: Z

11. Guided translation

a. B____ s_____ : *Good health*

b. S_ p_____ : *If I could*

c. D_____ d_ f_____ : *To stop smoking*

d. P____ m_____ : *To improve*

e. M_ s_____ : *My health*

f. C_____ d_____ : *To eat sweets*

g. P_____ t_____ e_____ :
To have energy

h. E_____ d_ b_____ a_____ :
To avoid drinking alcohol

i. J_____ v_____ : *Green beans*

j. E_ n_____ d_____ : *It's necessary to sleep*

12. Translate into Spanish

a. To have good health, I try to exercise regularly

b. I eat a lot of fruit and vegetables every day

c. I usually sleep eight hours a night and I always drink a lot of water

d. To stay in shape, I try to get enough rest

e. In the future, I am going to stop smoking

f. To have energy, I eat healthy food

g. I am going to make an effort to eat fewer sweets

h. I am going to stop drinking fizzy drinks and alcohol

i. If I could, I would cook more myself at home

j. To improve my health, I am going to do more sport

 THE LANGUAGE GYM

UNIT 2 - Test (/100)

---

1. Vocabulary recognition – Spanish to English gapped translation (/15)

a. Buena salud: _____ _____

b. Intento dormir: *I ____ to _____*

c. Debería evitar: *I _____ _____*

d. Si tuviera: ___ *I* _____

e. Menos dulces: _____ _____

f. Creo que: *I _____ _____*

g. Una dieta equilibrada: *A _____ _____*

h. Es necesario comer: _____ *to eat*

---

2. Syntax/Lexicogrammar – Split sentences (/5)

Si yo	**salud, tengo que dejar de fumar**
Creo	**tengo la intención de hacer más deporte**
Para mejorar mi	**pudiera, cocinaría más a menudo**
En el futuro	**comer más verduras**
Debo	**que estoy en forma**

---

3. Grammar/Morphology/Vocabulary – Tangled translation (/20)

a. Debo **quit** de **smoke**

b. Si **I had** más **time**…

c. Yo como **food organic**

d. Las **spinach** son ricas en **minerals**

e. **It is necessary** comer muchas **vegetables**

f. **I drink** mucha **water**

g. **I must** dejar de **drink** alcohol

h. Para **to be** en forma, debo hacer **more** deporte

i. **I am going to** hacer un **effort**

j. Como **many** productos **fresh**

---

4. Translate into Spanish (/60 – each full sentence – 6 points)

a. I believe that, in general, I am in good shape.

b. In order to improve my health, I must eat more fruit.

c. If I could, I would do sport more frequently.

d. I quite like eggs because they are rich in protein.

e. In the future, I am going to avoid fried food and sweets.

f. If I had more time, I would do more cycling.

g. I should avoid sweets and fatty foods.

h. In order to have energy, I sleep eight hours a night.

i. Generally, I have a healthy diet and do enough sport.

j. I don't eat sugar because it isn't healthy.

 THE LANGUAGE GYM

ANSWERS - Unit 2. Healthy/unhealthy living - Foundation

1. Match (section 1)
Duermo – *I sleep*   Evito – *I avoid*   No como – *I don't eat*   La comida frita – *Fried food*
Me relajo – *I relax*   Grasa – *Fat*   En mi ordenador – *On my computer*
Salgo – *I go out*   Hago ejercicio – *I exercise*   Una dieta – *A diet*

2. Gapped translation (section 1)
a. *I avoid **fried food***   b. *I don't eat too much **fat***   c. *I follow a **healthy** diet*
d. *I eat five portions of fruit and **vegetables** per day*   e. *I **exercise***   f. *I **relax** after school*   g. *I don't take **drugs***

3. Complete the sentences with a suitable verb and translate them into English (section 2)
a. Yo no **bebo** mucho alcohol: *I don't drink a lot of alcohol*
b. Yo siempre **estoy** estresado/a: *I am always stressed*
c. Yo **como** muchos dulces: *I eat sweets*
d. Yo **fumo** muchos cigarrillos: *I smoke a lot of cigarettes*
e. Yo **paso** mucho tiempo en las redes sociales: *I spend a lot of time on social media*
f. Yo **bebo/tomo** mucha Coca Cola: *I drink a lot of Coke*

4. Tick every sentence which refers to a healthy habit
a. X   b. √   c. X   d. X   e. X   f. √

5. Complete the table (section 1)
I sleep eight hours each night: **Duermo ocho horas cada noche**   *I relax:* Me relajo
I don't eat too much fat: No como demasiada grasa   *I follow a healthy diet:* **Sigo una dieta saludable**
I go out with my friends: Salgo con mis amigos   *I don't take drugs:* **No tomo drogas**
I exercise regularly: **Hago ejercicio regularmente**   *I avoid fried foods:* Evito la comida frita

6. Broken words (section 3)
a. Salu**dable**   b. No es **sano**   c. **Bueno**   d. No**civo**   e. Pel**igroso**   f. **Dul**ce   g. Malo   h. **Equi**librado
i. **Cans**ado   j. Gra**sie**nto

7. Gapped English to Spanish translation
a. **Duermo** ocho horas por **noche**   b. No **fumo** cigarillos   c. Evito la **comida frita**
d. **Paso** horas en las **redes sociales**   e. Hago **ejercicio** frecuentemente   f. La comida frita no es **sana**
g. Como cinco porciones de **verduras**   h. **Salgo** con mis **amigos**   i. No **bebo** mucho **alcohol**
j. No **duermo** lo suficiente

8. Write the one word missing in each sentence
a. duermo   b. fumo   c. es   d. redes   e. sigo/tengo   f. como/tomo/consumo   g. con

9. Guided translation
a. Bueno   b. Malo   c. Salud   d. Dieta   e. Nocivo   f. Dulce   g. Cansado/a   h. Drogas   i. Tiempo
j. Saludable

10. Translate into Spanish
a. Duermo por lo menos ocho horas cada noche.
c. No fumo cigarrillos
e. Paso mucho tiempo en las redes sociales y en mi (teléfono) móvil.
g. Hago ejercicio regularmente, pero como muchos dulces
i. Como cinco porciones de frutas y verduras al día
k. Las patatas fritas no son sanas porque son grasientas

b. Siempre estoy cansado/a y estresado/a
d. Evito la comida frita y los dulces
f. Sigo una dieta saludable
h. No tomo drogas, pero a veces fumo
j. No bebo/tomo refrescos
l. Paso una hora al día en internet

ANSWERS - Unit 2. Healthy/unhealthy living - Higher

1. Match

Dormir – *To sleep*   Evitar – *To avoid*   Fumar – *To smoke*   Mejorar – *To improve*

Descansar – *To rest*   Dejar de fumar – *To stop smoking*   Hacer un esfuerzo – *To make an effort*

Cocinar – *To cook*   Mantenerme en forma – *To stay in shape*

2. Gapped translation

a. *water* b. *nuts* c. *shape* d. *health* e. *smoking* f. *eggs* g. *green beans* h. *spinach*

3. Broken words

a. Salu**dable**   b. Alc**ohol**   c. Dul**ces**   d. Verd**uras**   e. Norm**almente**   f. En el f**uturo**

g. Dor**mir**   h. Hue**vos**   i. Espin**acas**   j. Fr**utos secos**   k. **Agua**   l. Fum**ar**

4. Complete with a suitable word

a. Bebo b. en c. los d. la e. dormir f. saludables g. por/cada h. buena

5. Translate into English

a. *Spinach* b. *Sweets*   c. *If I could* d. *Health*   e. *Myself* f. *Eggs* g. *Water* h. *Vegetables* i. *To smoke*

j. *Healthy food* k. *I would cook* l. *I intend to*

6. Missing vowels

a. Los dulces b. Es necesario c. Si pudiera d. Menos e. Fumar f. En el futuro

7. Anagrams

a. Dulces   b. Espinacas   c. Fumar   d. Dormir   e. Menos   f. Descansar   g. Salud

8. Sentence puzzle

a. Para mantenerse sano, es necesario descansar lo suficiente   b. Si pudiera, cocinaría más yo mismo

c. Todos los días, como mucha fruta y verdura   d. En el futuro tengo la intención de dejar de fumar

e. Como alimentos sanos para mantenerme en forma   f. Normalmente bebo zumo de naranja

9. Complete the table

Spinach: **Espinacas**   *If I could:* **Si pudiera**   *To stop:* **Dejar (de)**   *To rest:* **Descansar**   *To smoke:* **Fumar**

Good health: **Buena salud**   *To improve:* **Mejorar**   *Fatty foods:* **Alimentos grasos**

To stay in shape: **Mantenerse en forma**

10. Wordsearch

E		Z	U	M	O	
S					N	
P	S	M			E	D
I		E			U	
N		N	R	L	B	E
A		O	A		D	
C		S		R		
A	G	U	A			
S			J		M	
	E				U	
D					F	

To be: **Ser**
Good: **Bueno**
Less: **Menos**
To stop: **Dejar de**
To smoke: **Fumar**
Health: **Salud**
Spinach: **Espinacas**
Water: **Agua**
Juice: **Zumo**

11. Guided translation

a. Buena salud b. Si pudiera c. Dejar de fumar d. Para mejorar e. Mi salud f. Comer dulces

g. Para tener energía h. Evitar de beber alcohol i. Judías verdes j. Es necesario dormir

12. Translate into Spanish

a. Para tener una buena salud, intento hacer ejercicio regularmente.

b. Como mucha fruta y verdura todos los días.

c. Suelo dormir ocho horas cada noche y siempre bebo mucha agua.

d. Para mantenerme en forma, intento descansar lo suficiente.

e. En el futuro, voy a dejar de fumar. f. Para tener energía, como comida saludable.

g. Voy a hacer un esfuerzo para comer menos dulces. h. Voy a dejar de beber refrescos y alcohol.

i. Si pudiera, cocinaría más yo mismo en casa. j. Para mejorar mi salud, voy a hacer más deporte.

ANSWERS - UNIT 2 - Test (/100)

1. Vocabulary recognition - Spanish to English gapped translation (/15)

a. Buena salud: **Good health**

b. Intento dormir: I **try** to **sleep**

c. Debería evitar: I **should avoid**

d. Si tuviera: **If I had**

e. Menos dulces: **Fewer sweets**

f. Creo que: I **believe that**

g. Una dieta equilibrada: A **balanced diet**

h. Es necesario comer: **It is necessary** to eat **(1 point)**

2. Syntax/Lexicogrammar – Split sentences (/5)

Si yo	pudiera, cocinaría más a menudo
Creo	que estoy en forma
Para mejorar mi	salud, tengo que dejar de fumar
En el futuro	tengo la intención de hacer más deporte
Debo	comer más verduras

3. Grammar/Morphology/Vocabulary – Tangled translation (/20)

a. Debo **dejar** de **fumar**

b. Si **tuviera** más **tiempo**…

c. Yo como **comida biológica**

d. Las **espinacas** son ricas en **minerales**

e. **Es necesario** comer muchas **verduras**

f. **Bebo** mucha **agua**

g. **Debo** dejar de **beber** alcohol

h. Para **estar** en forma, debo hacer **más** deporte

i. **Voy a** hacer un **esfuerzo**

j. Como **muchos** productos **frescos**

4. Translate into Spanish (/60 – each full sentence – 6 points)

a. Creo que, por lo general estoy en forma.

b. Para mejorar mi salud, debo comer más fruta.

c. Si pudiera, haría deporte con más frecuencia.

d. Me gustan bastante los huevos porque son ricos en proteínas.

e. En el futuro voy a evitar la comida frita y los dulces.

f. Si tuviera más tiempo, haría más ciclismo.

g. Debo evitar los dulces y los alimentos grasos.

h. Para tener energía, duermo ocho horas por/cada noche.

i. En general, sigo/tengo una dieta sana y hago bastante deporte.

j. No como azúcar porque no es saludable.

 THE LANGUAGE GYM

Unit 3. Young people and fashion

KEY VOCABULARY-Foundation

1. La ropa (clothes)
Un abrigo: *A coat*
Un jersey: *A jumper*
Un vestido: *A dress*
Una blusa: *A blouse*
Una camisa: *A shirt*
Una falda: *A skirt*
Unos pantalones: *Trousers*
Unos pantalones cortos: *Shorts*
Unos zapatos: *Shoes*
Unas zapatillas de deporte: *Trainers*

2. Los colores (colours)
Amarillo: *Yellow*
Azul: *Blue*
Gris: *Grey*
Negro: *Black*
Rosa: *Pink*
Verde: *Green*

3. Los accesorios (accessories)
Un bolso: *A handbag*
Un collar: *A necklace*
Un reloj: *A watch*
Una gorra: *A cap*
Una mochila: *A backpack*
Unos pendientes: *Earrings*

4. Adjetivos importantes
Anticuado/a: *Unfashionable*
Ajustado/a: *Close-fitting*
Bonito/a: *Beautiful*
Caro/a: *Expensive*
Cómodo/a: *Comfortable*
Feo/a: *Ugly*
Guay: *Cool*
Nuevo/a: *New*
Viejo/a: *Old*

5. Expresiones esenciales
Barato/a: *Cheap*
De moda: *Fashionable / Trendy*
Llevo: *I wear*
Me gusta: *I like*
No me gusta: *I don't like*
Nunca llevo: *I never wear*
Prefiero: *I prefer*
Ropa de marca: *Branded clothes*

1. Match

Llevo pantalones	*It's beautiful*
Es bonito/a	*I wear a dress*
Llevo un reloj	*I wear a necklace*
Llevo un vestido	*It's unfashionable*
Es anticuado	*I wear a backpack*
Llevo una mochila	*I wear a watch*
Llevo una gorra	*I wear a blouse*
Es nuevo/a	*I wear trousers*
Llevo una camisa	*It's new*
Llevo una blusa	*I wear a shirt*
Llevo un collar	*It's fashionable*
Está de moda	*I wear a cap*

2. Work out the colours and translate into English as shown in the example

e.g. Un vestido **rigs**: Un vestido **gris**: *A grey dress*

a. Un jersey **lloamari**:

b. Una mochila **dever** y **grena**:

c. Una gorra **luaz**:

d. Un vestido **oroj**:

e. Unos pantalones cortos **clanbos**:

f. Una camisa **osar**:

3. Circle the correct translation

a. Un reloj: *a watch / a bracelet / a dress*

b. Una gorra: *a backpack / shorts / a cap*

c. Viejo: *new / old / nice*

d. Nuevo: *new / old / nice*

e. De moda: *ugly / fashionable / old*

f. Ajustado: *close-fitting / new / comfortable*

g. Una blusa: *trousers / shorts / a blouse*

4. Complete the words and translate into English

a. Una gor_ _ nu_ _ _ : *A new cap*

b. Un rel_ _ de mo_ _ : *A fashionable watch*

c. Un bo_ _ _ _ vesti_ _ rosa: *A beautiful pink dress*

d. Pendien_ _ _ ca _ _ _ _ : *Expensive earrings*

e. Lle_ _ pantalones ajusta_ _ _ : *I am wearing close-fitting trousers*

f. Ro_ _ de ma_ _ _ : *Branded clothes*

g. Una cam_ _ _ anticu_ _ _ : *An unfashionable shirt*

THE LANGUAGE GYM

5. Faulty translation – Correct the incorrect translations
(Note: not all the translations are wrong)

a. Llevo un vestido de moda: *I wear a fashionable vest*

b. Ella lleva un feo vestido rosa: *She wears a beautiful pink dress*

c. Él lleva ropa de marca: *He wears branded clothes*

d. Es un reloj nuevo: *It is a new backpack*

e. Estos zapatos son nuevos: *These shoes are old*

f. Ella lleva ropa barata: *They wear cheap clothes*

g. No llevo gorra: *I don't wear a cap*

6. Missing vowels

a. _n v_st_d_ (a dress)

b. z_p_t_s (shoes)

c. _n c_ll_r (a necklace)

d. _n r_l_j (a watch)

e. _n b_ls_ (a handbag)

f. _n_ f_ld_ (a skirt)

g. _n_ m_ch_l_ (a backpack)

7. Translate into English

a. Zapatos bonitos de moda

b. Una nueva gorra de marca

c. Un viejo vestido negro

d. Una falda verde anticuada

e. Un bonito collar de moda

f. Una bonita chaqueta azul

g. Unas zapatillas de deporte guays

8. Correct the adjectives so they agree with the noun in gender

e.g. Un vestido *bonita* – Un vestido **bonito**

a. Un reloj *nueva* - _____

b. Un vestido *roja* - _____

c. Una falda *viejo* - _____

d. Una gorra *anticuado* - _____

e. Una camisa *bonito* - _____

f. Una chaqueta *nuevo* - _____

9. Sentence puzzle

a. un viejo Llevo marrón reloj
I wear an old brown watch

b. Ella una falda no lleva vieja
She doesn't wear an old skirt

c. Tu vestido lleva un madre bonito
Your mother is wearing a beautiful dress

d. anticuados lleva pantalones Mi padre negros
My father is wearing unfashionable black trousers

e. ropa de Nosotros marca llevamos
We wear branded clothes

f. Mi nuevas zapatillas de hermana lleva deporte
My sister is wearing new trainers

11. Translate into Spanish

a. I am wearing a pink blouse and black shoes

b. We are wearing our new white trainers

c. He is wearing a new cap

d. Usually, I wear a white shirt, blue jeans and black shoes

e. She is wearing a new watch, a new necklace and new earrings

f. My father wears unfashionable clothes

g. My mother is wearing an old yellow dress

h. My brother always wears cool clothes

10. Guided translation

a. A beautiful dress: *U__ v_____ b_____*

b. An old coat: *U__ a_____ v_____*

c. A new skirt: *U___ f_____ n_____*

d. A fashionable shirt: *U__ c_____ d__ m____*

e. A new necklace: *U__ c_____ n_____*

f. An unfashionable watch: *U__ r____ a_____*

g. A red handbag: *U__ b_____ r_____*

THE LANGUAGE GYM

KEY VOCABULARY - Higher

1. ¿Qué es la moda? (*What is fashion?*)
El estilo: *Look/style*
El estilo de vestirse: *Clothing style*
El maquillaje: *Make-up*
La apariencia: *Appearance*
La joyería: *Jewellery*
La moda: *Fashion*
La ropa: *Clothes*
Las marcas: *Brands*
Los accesorios: *Accessories*
Los bolsos: *Handbags*
Los tatuajes: *Tattoos*
Los vestidos: *Dresses*

2. ¿Por qué es importante la moda?
Los jóvenes llevan ropa de marca:
Young people wear branded clothes
Muchos jóvenes llevan ropa de moda:
Many young people wear fashionable clothes
Es una manera: *It's a way*
-de atraer a los chicos/chicas: *to attract boys/girls*
-de encajar en un grupo: *to fit into a group*
La moda permite: *Fashion allows one to*
-expresarse: *to express oneself*
-hacerse notar: *to get noticed*
La mayoría de los adolescentes se viste para causar impresión:
Most teenagers dress to impress
Los accesorios ayudan a: *Accessories help to*
-definir la propia identidad: *define one's identity*
-diferenciarse de los demás / destacar: *stand out*
-mejorar la imagen: *improve one's image*

3. Las desventajas de la moda
Es cara: *It's expensive*
Nos anima a malgastar el dinero:
It encourages us to waste money
Pone presión a los adolescentes:
It puts pressure on teenagers
Puede convertirse en una adicción:
It can become an addiction

4. Verbos importantes
Llevar: *To wear*
Maquillarse: *To put make-up on*
Vestirse: *To get dressed*

1. Match (section 1)

Llevar	*Clothes*
El estilo	*Brands*
La moda	*Dresses*
La ropa	*Fashion*
La joyería	*Handbags*
Las marcas	*Look*
Los bolsos	*Jewellery*
Maquillarse	*To put make-up on*
Los vestidos	*To wear*

2. Faulty translation (section 2) – Correct the wrong translations
a. Muchos jóvenes: *Some young people*
b. Hacerse notar: *To be accepted*
c. Mejorar: *To wear*
d. Encajar en un grupo: *To appeal to others*
e. Ropa de marca: *Branded clothes*
f. Los jóvenes se visten: *Young people like*
g. De moda: *Fashionable*

3. Broken words (section 1)
a. El maqui_ _ _ _ _
b. Los bol_ _ _
c. La joye _ _ _
d. La mo_ _
e. El est_ _ _
f. Los tatu_ _ _ _
g. Not_ _
h. Compl_ _ _ _
i. Las mar_ _ _
j. Los acces_ _ _ _ _
k. Los vestid_ _
l. La ro_ _

4. Complete with the missing words (sections 2 and 3)
a. Muchos _____ : *Many young people*
b. Los accesorios _____ : *Accessories help*
c. Puede _____ : *It can become*
d. Para _____ : *To stand out*
e. _____ a las chicas: *To attract girls*
f. Es una _____ de: *It is a way to*
g. _____ a los otros: *To appeal to others*
h. Pone _____ : *It puts pressure*

5. Translate into English (all sections)

a. La moda:

b. Puede convertirse:

c. Destacar:

d. Atraer a los chicos:

e. Hacerse notar:

f. La joyería:

g. Es una manera:

h. Malgastar:

i. Los tatuajes:

j. Mejorar su imagen:

k. El estilo:

l. De moda:

6. Missing vowels (section 3)

a. M_lg_st_r: *To waste*

b. C_r_: *Expensive*

c. C_nv_rt_rs_: *To become*

d. D_n_r: *Money*

e. P_n_: *It puts*

f. C_ _ st_: *It costs*

7. Anagrams (section 1)

a. yeríaJo

b. oMad

c. opaR

d. dositVes

e. jesTuata

f. liotEs

g. carMas

h. cesAcoiros

8. Sentence puzzle (all sections)

a. Los ayudan la propia identidad accesorios a definir

b. los demás Es una de complacer a forma

c. a malgastar Nos anima el dinero

d. Los tatuajes son notar de hacerse una manera

e. una adicción convertirse en Puede

f. es moda La cara

g. La imagen mejorar a la moda ayuda

9. Complete the table

English	Español
Jewellery	
	Estilo
	Puede convertirse en
To get dressed	
Tattoos	
	Mejorar su imagen
	Es una manera de
Others	
	Para expresarse

10. Wordsearch – Find the Spanish for the listed words

L	A	I	M	A	G	E	N
C	A	D	B	P	M	P	L
O	G	C	E	O	A	R	A
R	S	A	R	R	D	I	O
B	Á	O	M	A	O	N	C
A	M	N	E	L	M	P	U
T	E	S	I	C	E	I	E
A	D	T	A	Ü	D	N	S
N	S	R	E	R	G	A	T
E	O	L	I	T	S	E	A
R	L	L	E	V	A	R	N

Look: E

Fashionable: D

Others: Los d

Brand: M

Expensive: C

To wear: L

(It) costs: C

Image: La i

Clothes: La r

11. Guided translation

a. *Fashion is expensive*: L_ m_ _ _ e_ c_ _ _

b. *To appeal to others*: C_ _ _ _ _ _ _ _ a los d_ _ _ _

c. *Jewellery*: J_ _ _ _ _ _

d. *It allows to express oneself*: P_ _ _ _ _ _ e_ _ _ _ _ _ _ _ _

e. *Branded clothes*: R_ _ _ de m_ _ _ _

f. *To improve one's image*: M_ _ _ _ _ _ s_ i_ _ _ _ _

g. *To get noticed*: H_ _ _ _ _ _ n_ _ _ _

h. *Pressure*: P_ _ _ _ _ _

i. *It can become*: P_ _ _ _ c_ _ _ _ _ _ _ _ _ _

12. Translate into Spanish

a. Fashion can become an addiction

b. Many teenagers wear branded clothes

c. Is it a way to fit into a group

d. Tattoos allow one to get noticed

e. Fashion is a way to attract boys

f. Sadly, it encourages us to waste money

g. Clothes allow us to improve our image

h. Fashion is expensive

 THE LANGUAGE GYM

UNIT 3 - Test (/100)

1. Vocabulary recognition – Spanish to English translation (/15)

a. Actualmente:

b. Atraer:

c. La moda:

d. Última:

e. Permite:

f. Ropa:

g. Marca:

h. Es necesario:

i. Joyería:

j. Imagen:

k. Jóvenes:

l. Puede:

m. Dejar:

n. Zapatos:

o. Complacer:

2. Syntax/Lexicogrammar – Split sentences (/5)

Sigo las últimas	**la moda**
La ropa ayuda a	**la moda puede poner presión a los adolescentes**
Personalmente, no me gusta	**tendencias de la moda**
Lo triste es que	**de expresarse**
El estilo es una manera	**diferenciarse de los demás**

3. Grammar/Morphology/Vocabulary – Tangled translation (/20)

a. Me gusta llevar **pretty dresses** rojos

b. Yo no **wear** ropa de **brand**

c. Yo no **follow** la **fashion**

d. Me gustan la **jewellery** y los **tattoos**

e. El estilo es una **way** de **attract** a las chicas

f. **It's** una manera de **express oneself**

g. **Many** jóvenes visten para **impress (cause impression)**

h. Los accesorios **help** a diferenciarse de los **others**

i. **It can become** en una adicción

j. El estilo los ayuda a **fit in** un grupo

4. Translate into Spanish (/ 60 – each full sentence – 6 points)

a. Fashion can become an addiction for many young people.

b. Fashion is a way to define one's identity.

c. Nowadays, many teenagers carry branded bags.

d. I don't wear jewellery, but I have two tattoos.

e. Clothes help us to improve our image.

f. For many young people, clothing style is very important.

g. It is a way to get noticed.

h. I don't follow fashion because it is very expensive.

i. Accessories help us stand out from others.

j. We must let young people develop their own identity.

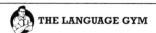
THE LANGUAGE GYM

21

ANSWERS - Unit 3. Young people and fashion - Foundation

1. Match

Llevo pantalones – ***I wear trousers***   Es bonito/a – ***It's beautiful***   Llevo un reloj – ***I wear a watch***
Llevo un vestido – ***I wear a dress***   Es anticuado – ***It's unfashionable***
Llevo una mochila – ***I wear a backpack***   Llevo una gorra – ***I wear a cap***   Es nuevo/a – ***It's new***
Llevo una camisa – ***I wear a shirt***   Llevo una blusa – ***I wear a blouse***
Llevo un collar – ***I wear a necklace***   Está de moda – ***It's fashionable***

2. Work out the colours and translate into English as shown in the example

e.g. Un vestido **rigs**: Un vestido **gris**: *A grey dress*

a. Un jersey **lloamari**: Un jersey **amarillo**: *A yellow jumper*

b. Una mochila **dever** y **grena**: Una mochila **verde** y **negra**: *A green and black backpack*

c. Una gorra **luaz**: Una gorra **azul**: *A blue cap*

d. Un vestido **oroj**: Un vestido **rojo**: *A red dress*

e. Unos pantalones cortos **clanbos**: Unos pantalones cortos **blancos**: *White shorts*

f. Una camisa **osar**: Una camisa **rosa**: *A pink shirt*

3. Circle the correct translation

a. Un reloj: *a watch*   b. Una gorra: *a cap*   c. Viejo: *old*   d. Nuevo: *new*

e. De moda: *fashionable*   f. Ajustado: *close-fitting*   g. Una blusa: *a blouse*

4. Complete the words and translate into English

a. Una gor**ra** nu**eva**: *A new cap*   b. Un rel**oj** de mo**da**: *A fashionable watch*

c. Un bo**nito** vesti**do** rosa: *A beautiful pink dress*   d. Pendien**tes** ca**ros**: *Expensive earrings*

e. Lle**vo** pantalones ajusta**dos**: *I am wearing close-fitting trousers*   f. **Ro**pa de ma**rca**: *Branded clothes*

g. Una cam**isa** anticu**ada**: *An unfashionable shirt*

5. Faulty translation

a. Llevo un vestido de moda: *I wear a fashionable **dress*** b. Ella lleva un feo vestido rosa: *She wears an **ugly** pink dress* c. √ d. Es un reloj nuevo: *It is a new **watch*** e. Estos zapatos son nuevos: *These shoes are **new*** f. Ella lleva ropa barata: ***She wears** cheap clothes* g. √

6. Missing vowels

a. **Un vestido** b. **Zapatos** c. **Un collar** d. **Un reloj** e. **Un bolso** f. **Una falda** g. **Una mochila**

7. Translate into English

a. *Beautiful fashionable shoes*   b. *A new branded cap*   c. *An old black dress*   d. *An unfashionable green skirt*

e. *A beautiful fashionable necklace*   f. *A beautiful blue jacket*   g. *Cool trainers*

8. Correct the adjectives so they agree with the noun in gender

e.g. Un vestido bonit**o**   a. Un reloj nuev**o**   b. Un vestido roj**o**   c. Una falda viej**a**

d. Una gorra anticuad**a**   e. Una camisa bonit**a**   f. Una chaqueta nuev**a**

9. Sentence puzzle

a. Llevo un viejo reloj marrón   b. Ella no lleva una falda vieja   c. Tu madre lleva un vestido bonito
d. Mi padre lleva pantalones negros anticuados   e. Nosotros llevamos ropa de marca
f. Mi hermana lleva zapatillas de deporte nuevas

10. Guided translation

a. Un vestido bonito   b. Un abrigo viejo   c. Una falda nueva   d. Una camisa de moda

e. Un collar nuevo   f. Un reloj anticuado   g. Un bolso rojo

11. Translate into Spanish

a. Llevo una blusa rosa y zapatos negros   b. Llevamos nuestras zapatillas de deporte blancas nuevas

c. Él lleva una gorra nueva   d. Normalmente llevo una camisa blanca, vaqueros azules y zapatos negros

e. Ella lleva un reloj nuevo, un collar nuevo y pendientes nuevos   f. Mi padre lleva ropa anticuada

g. Mi madre lleva un viejo vestido amarillo   h. Mi hermano siempre lleva ropa guay

 **THE LANGUAGE GYM**

ANSWERS - Unit 3. Young people and fashion - Higher

1. Match (section 1)
Llevar – *To wear*   El estilo – *Look*   La moda – *Fashion*   La ropa – *Clothes*   La joyería – *Jewellery*
Las marcas – *Brands*   Los bolsos – *Handbags*   Maquillarse – *To put make-up on*   Los vestidos – *Dresses*

2. Faulty translation (section 2)
a. Muchos jóvenes: *Many* young people   b. Hacerse notar: *To get noticed*   c. Mejorar: *To improve*
d. √   e. √   f. Los jóvenes se visten: *Young people dress*   g. √

3. Broken words (section 1)
a. El maqui**llaje**   b. Los bol**sos**   c. La joye**ría**   d. La mo**da**   e. El esti**lo**   f. Los tatu**ajes**   g. No**tar**
h. Compl**acer**   i. Las mar**cas**   j. Los acces**orios**   k. Los vestid**os**   l. La ro**pa**

4. Complete with the missing words (sections 2 and 3)
a. Muchos **jóvenes**   b. Los accesorios **ayudan**   c. Puede **convertirse**   d. Para **destacar/diferenciarse de los demás**   e. **Atraer** a las chicas   f. Es una **manera** de   g. **Complacer** a los otros   h. Pone **presión**

5. Translate into English (all sections)
a. Fashion   b. It can become   c. To stand out   d. To attract boys   e. To get noticed   f. Jewellery
g. It's a way   h. To waste   i. Tattoos   j. To improve one's look   k. The look/style   l. Fashionable

6. Missing vowels (section 3)
a. Malgastar   b. Caro   c. Convertirse   d. Dinero   e. Pone   f. Cuesta

7. Anagrams (section 1)
a. Joyería   b. Moda   c. Ropa   d. Vestidos   e. Tatuajes   f. Estilo   g. Marcas   h. Accesorios

8. Sentence puzzle (all sections)
a. Los accesorios ayudan a definir la propia identidad   b. Es una forma de complacer a los demás
c. Nos anima a malgastar el dinero   d. Los tatuajes son una manera de hacerse notar
e. Puede convertirse en una adicción   f. La moda es cara   g. La moda ayuda a mejorar la imagen

9. Complete the table
Jewellery: **Joyería**   *Look/Style:* **Estilo**   *It can become:* **Puede convertirse en**   *To get dressed:* **Vestirse**
Tattoos: **Tatuajes**   *Improve one's image:* **Mejorar su imagen**   *It's a way of:* **Es una manera de**
Others: **Otros / Demás**   *To express oneself:* **Para expresarse**

10. Wordsearch

L	A	I	M	A	G	E	N
	A			P			
		C		O	A		
	S		R	R	D		
	Á			A	O		C
	M			L	M		U
	E		I	C	E		E
	D	T	A		D		S
	S	R					T
	O	L	I	T	S	E	A
	L	L	E	V	A	R	

Look: **Estilo**
Fashionable: **De moda**
Others: **Los demás**
Brand: **Marca**
Expensive: **Caro**
To wear: **Llevar**
(It) costs: **Cuesta**
Image: **La imagen**
Clothes: **La ropa**

11. Guided translation
a. La moda es cara   b. Complacer a los demás   c. Joyería   d. Permite expresarse
e. Ropa de marca   f. Mejorar su imagen   g. Hacerse notar   h. Presión
i. Puede convertirse

12. Translate into Spanish
a. La moda puede convertirse en una adicción   b. Muchos adolescentes llevan ropa de marca
c. Es una manera de encajar en un grupo   d. Los tatuajes permiten hacerse notar
e. La moda es una manera de atraer a los chicos   f. Desafortunadamente, nos anima a malgastar el dinero
g. La ropa nos permite mejorar nuestra imagen   h. La moda es cara

THE LANGUAGE GYM

ANSWERS - UNIT 3 - Test (/100)

1. Vocabulary recognition – Spanish to English translation (/15)

a. Actualmente: **Currently**

b. Atraer: **To attract**

c. La moda: **Fashion**

d. Última : **Last**

e. Permite: **Allows**

f. Ropa: **Clothes**

g. Marca: **Brand**

h. Es necesario: **It's necessary**

i. Joyería: **Jewellery**

j. Imagen: **Image**

k. Jóvenes: **Young people**

l. Puede: **Can**

m. Dejar: **To quit**

n. Zapatos: **Shoes**

o. Complacer: **To appeal**

2. Syntax/Lexicogrammar – Split sentences (/5)

Sigo las últimas	**tendencias de la moda**
La ropa ayuda a	**diferenciarse de los demás**
Personalmente, no me gusta	**la moda**
Lo triste es que	**la moda puede poner presión a los adolescentes**
El estilo es una manera	**de expresarse**

3. Grammar/Morphology/Vocabulary – Tangled translation (/20)

a. Me gusta llevar **bonitos vestidos** rojos

b. Yo no **llevo** ropa de **marca**

c. Yo no **sigo** la **moda**

d. Me gustan la **joyería** y los **tatuajes**

e. El estilo es una **manera** de **atraer** a las chicas

f. **Es** una manera de **expresarse**

g. **Muchos** jóvenes visten para **causar impresión**

h. Los accesorios **ayudan** a diferenciarse de los **demás**

i. **Puede convertirse** en una adicción

j. El estilo los ayuda a **encajar en** un grupo

4. Translate into Spanish (/ 60 – each full sentence – 6 points)

a. La moda puede convertirse en una adicción para muchos jóvenes.

b. La moda es una manera de definir la propia identidad.

c. Actualmente muchos adolescentes llevan bolsos de marca.

d. Yo no llevo joyería pero tengo dos tatuajes.

e. La ropa nos ayuda a mejorar nuestra imagen.

f. Para muchos jóvenes, el estilo de vestir es muy importante.

g. Es una manera de hacerse notar.

h. No sigo la moda porque es muy cara.

i. Los accesorios ayudan a diferenciarse de los demás.

j. Debemos dejar que los jóvenes desarrollen su propia identidad.

Unit 4. Environment: Global problems

KEY VOCABULARY - Foundation

1. Las actividades contaminantes
El transporte: *Transport*

El uso de pesticidas:
The use of pesticides

El uso de productos químicos:
The use of chemical products

La agricultura intensiva:
Intensive farming

La deforestación: *Deforestation*

La liberación de aguas residuales:
The release of wastewater

Las fábricas: *Factories*

Los atascos: *Traffic jams*

Los residuos industriales:
Industrial waste

2. Animales en peligro
Las ballenas azules: *Blue whales*
Los orangutanes: *Orangutans*
Los osos polares: *Polar bears*

3. Los problemas
El aumento de la población:
The population increase

El calentamiento global:
Global warming

El deshielo de los polos:
The melting of the ice caps

El efecto invernadero:
The greenhouse effect

El sobreconsumo:
Overconsumption

Las sequías: *Droughts*

La subida del nivel del mar:
The sea level rise

Los incendios forestales: *Forest fires*

Las inundaciones: *Floods*

4. Adjetivos útiles
Artificial: *Artificial*
Natural: *Natural*

5. Verbos importantes
Amenazar: *To threaten*
Aumentar: *To increase*
Causar: *To cause*
Consumir: *To consume*
Contribuir: *To contribute*
Poner en peligro: *To endanger*
Proteger: *To protect*

1. Match

Los osos	*Industrial waste*
La agricultura intensiva	*Bears*
Los productos químicos	*Traffic jams*
Los residuos industriales	*Factories*
Las aguas residuales	*Blue whales*
Las ballenas azules	*Chemical products*
Las fábricas	*Intensive farming*
La liberación	*Wastewater*
Los atascos	*Release*

2. Spot and fix the incorrect translations (sections 1 & 2)

a. Los residuos industriales: *Industrial developments*

b. Las ballenas azules: *Blue birds*

c. Las fábricas: *Public transport*

d. La agricultura intensiva: *Intense traffic*

e. Los atascos: *The attacks*

f. La liberación de aguas residuales: *The release of waste rats*

g. El uso de pesticidas: *The use of pests*

3. Gapped translation (section 3)

a. El efecto invernadero: *The _____ effect*

b. La subida del nivel del mar: *The _____ _____ rise*

c. Las inundaciones frecuentes: *The frequent _____*

d. El sobreconsumo de alimentos: *The _____ of food*

e. El aumento de la población: *The population _____*

f. Los incendios forestales: *Forest _____*

g. El deshielo de los polos: *The _____ of the ice caps*

4. Translate into English

a. Efecto invernadero	h. Atascos
b. Amenazar	i. Los osos
c. Sequías	j. Productos
d. Incendios	k. El deshielo
e. Inundaciones	l. Aguas residuales
f. Ballenas	m. Nivel
g. Residuos	n. Fábricas

5. Complete and translate the phrases into English

a. Las seq _ _ _ _ :

b. El calen _ _ _ _ _ _ _ global:

c. El au _ _ _ _ _ de la población:

d. La _ _ forestación:

e. Los res _ _ _ _ _ industriales:

f. La sub _ _ _ del nivel del mar:

g. El desh _ _ _ _ de los polos:

h. Los incen _ _ _ _ forestales:

6. Break the flow

a. Elniveldelmar

b. Lososospolares

c. Lasballenasazules

d. Losincendiosforestales

e. Elaumentodelapoblación

f. Laliberacióndeaguasresiduales

g. Elusodeproductosquímicos

h. Elusodepesticidas

7. Missing vowels

a. L_ d_f_r_st_c_ _ n

b. L_s f_br_c_s

c. L_s b_ll_n_s _z_l_s

d. L_s r_s_d_ _s _nd_str_ _l_s

e. _l c_l_nt_m_ _nt_ gl_b_l

f. L_ l_b_r_c_ _n d_ _g_ _s r_s_d_ _l_s

g. _l d_sh_ _l_ d_ l_s p_l_s

8. Wordsearch – Find the Spanish for the listed words

S	E	Q	U	Í	A	S	P	E	S
O	F	L	I	L	Y	I	R	D	O
R	Á	T	R	D	N	E	A	L	I
A	B	N	O	Ü	G	B	L	A	D
N	R	E	S	I	D	U	O	S	N
G	I	O	G	N	E	R	P	N	E
U	C	D	M	O	P	D	O	O	C
T	A	N	A	G	U	A	S	R	N
O	S	E	R	P	A	R	O	D	I

Droughts: S

Polar bear: O

Fires: I

Waters: A

Factories: F

Waste: R

Sea: M

9. Add in the missing word

a. El _____ de los polos: *The melting of the ice caps*

b. La _____ del nivel del mar: *The sea level rise*

c. La liberación de aguas _____: *Release of wastewater*

d. Los _____ industriales: *Industrial waste*

e. El _____ de la población: *The population increase*

f. Las _____ azules: *Blue whales*

g. _____ las especies animales: *To threaten animal species*

10 Translate into Spanish

a. *Droughts*: S

b. *Release*: L

c. *Waste*: R

d. *To threaten*: A

e. *Warming*: C

f. *Increase*: A

g. *Melting*: D

h. *Waters*: A

i. *Traffic jams*: A

j. *Level*: N

k. *Sea*: M

l. *Effect*: E

m. *Greenhouse*: I

n. *Factories*: F

11. English to Spanish translation

a. The use of chemical products

b. Intensive farming

c. Global warming

d. The overconsumption of food

e. Industrial waste

f. The release of wastewater

g. Traffic jams contribute to air pollution

h. Fossil fuels contribute to greenhouse effect and global warming

i. The melting of the ice caps causes the increase in sea level

j. Blue whales and polar bears are endangered species

k. The increase in world population contributes to the exhaustion of natural resources

THE LANGUAGE GYM

KEY VOCABULARY - Higher

1. Los problemas mundiales *(global issues)*

El agotamiento de recursos naturales:
The exhaustion of natural resources

El calentamiento global: *Global warming*

El deshielo de los polos: *The melting of the ice caps*

El desperdicio de alimentos: *Food waste*

El efecto invernadero: *The greenhouse effect*

El malgasto de recursos: *The waste of resources*

La contaminación del aire / agua / suelo:
Air / water / soil pollution

La desaparición de especies vegetales:
The disappearance of plant species

La escasez de alimentos:
The shortage of foodstuffs

La extinción de especies animales:
The extinction of animal species

La pérdida de la biodiversidad:
The loss of biodiversity

La subida del nivel del mar: *The sea level rise*

Las inundaciones: *Floods*

2. Las causas

El aumento de la población mundial:
The world population increase

El sobreconsumo: *Overconsumption*

El tráfico aéreo: *Air traffic*

El transporte aéreo: *Air transport*

La agricultura: *Agriculture*

La caza: *Hunting*

La deforestación: *Deforestation*

La especie humana: *The human species*

La industria: *The industry*

Los gases de efecto invernadero:
Greenhouse gases

Los combustibles fósiles: *Fossil fuels*

3. Verbos importantes

Amenazar: *To threaten*

Crecer: *To grow*

Dejar una huella: *To leave a footprint*

Hacer (visible): *To make (visible)*

Jugar un papel: *To play a role*

Parar: *To stop*

Poner en peligro: *To endanger*

Ser causado/a por: *To be caused by*

1. Match (section 1)

Floods	*El efecto invernadero*
Greenhouse effect	*Las especies animales*
The rise	*Las inundaciones*
Soil	*Deshielo de los polos*
Melting of the ice caps	*La subida*
Warming	*El nivel del mar*
Sea level	*La desaparición*
Animal species	*El suelo*
Disappearance	*El calentamiento*

2. Gapped phrases (sections 1 & 2) – Complete and translate

a. El d_____ de alimentos

b. La e_____ humana

c. El t_____ aéreo

d. La contaminación del a_____ y del a_____

e. Los gases de efecto i_____

f. La s_____ del nivel del mar

3. Broken words (sections 1-3)

a. Inunda_ _ _ _ _ _   g. La ca_ _

b. Los ga_ _ _   h. Carret_ _ _

c. La pér_ _ _ _   i. La desa_ _ _ _ _ _ _

d. Combu_ _ _ _ _ _ _   j. Aér_ _

e. El niv_ _   k. Los ali_ _ _ _ _ _

f. La sub_ _ _   l. La esc_ _ _ _

4. Faulty translation – Correct the wrong translations (sections 2–3)

a. Poner en peligro: *To preserve*

b. El tráfico en la carretera: *Air traffic*

c. Jugar un papel: *To play a role*

d. Hacer visible: *To make visible*

e. Parar: *To start*

f. La caza: *Fishing*

g. Amenazar: *To protect*

 THE LANGUAGE GYM

5. Translate into English (all sections)

a. El transporte
b. La caza
c. Los combustibles
d. La huella
e. El efecto invernadero
f. El sobreconsumo
g. El calentamiento global
h. La especie
i. La población mundial
j. Parar
k. El agotamiento
l. Poner en peligro

6. Missing vowels

a. L_ _sp_c_ _
b. L_ c_z_
c. _l _g_t_m_ _nt_
d. L_s c_mb_st_bl_s
e. _l s_br_c_ns_m_
f. _l c_l_nt_m_ _nt_
g. L_ p_rd_d_

7. Anagrams

a. speeicsE
b. Nevli
c. Halelu
d. totaAmengoi
e. Custimbobles
f. Dsheielo
g. loPos
h. amentaCliento

8. Sentence puzzle

a. no población crecer La mundial deja de

b. invernadero efecto se la acelera por El actividad humana

c. El contaminación debe calentamiento global se a la

d. El zonas deshielo de los inundaciones polos provoca en las costeras

e. extinción animales fauna de especies amenaza la La diversidad de la

f. La océanos temperatura de los no para de cada aumentar año

9. Complete the table

English	Español
Hunting	
	Agotamiento
Global warming	
Fuels	
	Malgasto
Melting	
	Inundaciones
To increase	
	Pérdida

10. Wordsearch – Find the Spanish for the listed words

S	U	E	S	S	Y	D	O	C	N
D	I	V	E	R	S	I	D	A	D
E	L	E	N	A	G	N	N	Z	I
S	Z	M	A	R	A	U	G	A	M
H	U	E	L	L	A	N	L	R	A
I	A	M	A	F	Z	D	M	Z	N
E	N	I	E	R	I	A	N	P	Y
L	N	B	G	A	R	C	N	R	A
O	E	S	P	E	C	I	E	S	H
D	J	A	L	A	N	Ó	J	V	O
R	O	N	I	Ü	G	N	I	P	S

Hunting: C
Diversity: D
Melting: D
Species: E
Flood: I
Penguin: P
Water: A
Air: A
Footprint: H
Fauna: F

11. Guided translation

a. *Melting of the ice caps*:
E_ d_____ d_ l__ p_____
b. *The extinction of animal species*:
L__ e_____ d_ e_____ a_____
c. *Greenhouse gases*:
L___ g_____ d_ e_____ i_____
d. *To leave a footprint*:
D_____ u__ h_____
e. *Global warming*:
E__ c_____ g_____
f. *The ocean temperature*:
L__ t_____ d_ l_ o_____
g. *World population*:
L__ p_____ m_____

12. Translate into Spanish

a. The melting of the ice caps
b. (The) Human activity
c. The extinction of animal and plant species
d. The sea level rise
e. Global warming is a worrying phenomenon
f. The pollution of the air threatens our health
g. (The) Floods are becoming more and more common
h. There is a lot of waste of natural resources
i. To leave a footprint on the environment
j. Hunting puts in danger many animal species

 THE LANGUAGE GYM

UNIT 4 - Test (/100)

1. Vocabulary recognition - Spanish to English translation (/15)

a. El deshielo de los polos

b. Las fábricas

c. El efecto invernadero

d. Los residuos

e. Los atascos

f. Amenazar

g. Los incendios

h. La sequía

i. La desaparición

j. El mar

k. El paisaje

l. La escasez

m. Las inundaciones

n. El malgasto

o. El sobreconsumo

2. Syntax/Lexicogrammar – Split sentences (/5)

La población mundial no deja	**por la actividad humana**
El deshielo de los polos provoca	**prohibir las pesticidas**
El efecto invernadero se acelera	**de crecer**
Deberíamos	**de los recursos**
Hay que reducir el malgasto	**inundaciones**

3. Grammar/Morphology/Vocabulary – Tangled translation (/20)

a. Los **gases** de escape de **cars**

b. La **diversity** de la **fauna**

c. La **disappearance** de **species** vegetales

d. **There are** muchos **traffic jams**

e. El **increase** de la **population**

f. El agotamiento de **natural resources**

g. **In** las zonas **coastal**

h. El **waste** de **food**

i. Dejar una **footprint** en el **environment**

j. La **rise** del **level** del mar

k. La **temperature** de los **oceans**

l. La **shortage** de **food**

4. Translate into Spanish (/ 60 – each full sentence – 6 points)

a. Fossil fuels contribute to the greenhouse effect.

b. The melting of the ice caps causes the sea level rise.

c. Blue whales and polar bears are endangered species.

d. Traffic jams are an important cause of air pollution.

e. The population increase is the main cause of pollution.

f. Deforestation is one of the causes of global warming.

g. The ocean temperature keeps growing every day.

h. The sea level rise causes floods at the seaside.

i. The greenhouse effect is accelerated by pollution.

j. The exhaustion of natural resources is a great problem.

THE LANGUAGE GYM

ANSWERS - Unit 4. Environment: Global problems - Foundation

1. Match

Los osos – *Bears*   La agricultura intensiva – *Intensive farming*

Los productos químicos – *Chemical products*   Los residuos industriales – *Industrial waste*

Las aguas residuales – *Wastewater*   Las ballenas azules – *Blue whales*

Las fábricas – *Factories*   La liberación – *Release*   Los atascos – *Traffic jams*

2. Spot and fix the incorrect translations (sections 1 & 2)

a. *Industrial waste*   b. *Blue whales*   c. *Factories*   d. *Intensive farming*   e. *Traffic jams*

f. *The release of wastewater*   g. *The use of pesticides*

3. Gapped translation (section 3)

a. *The greenhouse effect*   b. *The sea level rise*   c. *The frequent floods*   d. *The overconsumption of food*

e. *The population increase*   f. *Forest fires*   g. *The melting of the ice caps*

4. Translate into English

a. *Greenhouse effect*   b. *To threaten*   c. *Droughts*   d. *Fires*   e. *Floods*   f. *Whales*   g. *Waste*   h. *Traffic jams*

i. *Bears*   j. *Products*   k. *Melting*   l. *Wastewater*   m. *Level*   n. *Factories*

5. Complete and translate the phrases into English

a. Las sequías: *Droughts*   b. El calentamiento global: *Global warming*

c. El aumento de la población: *The population increase*   d. La deforestación: *Deforestation*

e. Los residuos industriales: *Industrial waste*   f. La subida del nivel del mar: *The sea level rise*

g. El deshielo de los polos: *The melting of the ice caps*   h. Los incendios forestales: *Forest fires*

6. Break the flow

a. El nivel del mar   b. Los osos polares   c. Las ballenas azules   d. Los incendios forestales

e. El aumento de la población   f. La liberación de aguas residuales   g. El uso de productos químicos

h. El uso de pesticidas

7. Missing vowels

a. La deforestación   b. Las fábricas   c. Las ballenas azules   d. Los residuos industriales

e. El calentamiento global   f. La liberación de aguas residuales   g. El deshielo de los polos

8. Wordsearch

S	E	Q	U	Í	A	S		S
	F					R		O
	A					A		I
	B					L		D
	R	E	S	I	D	U	O	S	N
	I					P		E
	C		M			O		C
	A		A	G	U	A	S	N
	S		R			O		I

Droughts: **Sequías**
Polar bear: **Oso polar**
Fires: **Incendios**
Waters: **Aguas**
Factories: **Fábricas**
Waste: **Residuos**
Sea: **Mar**

9. Add in the missing word

a. El **deshielo** de los polos   b. La **subida** del nivel del mar   c. La liberación de aguas **residuales**

d. Los **residuos** industriales   e. El **aumento** de la población   f. Las **ballenas** azules

g. **Amenazar** las especies animales

10. Translate into Spanish

a. **Sequías**   b. **Liberación**   c. **Residuos**   d. **Amenazar**   e. **Calentamiento**   f. **Aumento**   g. **Deshielo**

h. **Aguas**   i. **Atascos**   j. **Nivel**   k. **Mar**   l. **Efecto**   m. **Invernadero**   n. **Fábricas**

11. English to Spanish translation

a. El uso de productos químicos   b. La agricultura intensiva   c. El calentamiento global

d. El sobreconsumo de alimentos   e. Los residuos industriales   f. La liberación de aguas residuales

g. Los atascos contribuyen a la contaminación del aire

h. Los combustibles fósiles contribuyen al efecto invernadero y al calentamiento global

i. El deshielo de los polos contribuye a la subida del nivel del mar

j. Las ballenas azules y los osos polares son animales en peligro

k. El aumento de la población mundial contribuye al agotamiento de los recursos naturales

ANSWERS - Unit 4. Environment: Global problems - Higher

1. Match (section 1)

Floods – **Las inundaciones**   *Greenhouse effect* – **El efecto invernadero**   *The rise* – **La subida**

Soil – **El suelo**   *Melting of the ice caps* – **El deshielo de los polos**   *Warming* – **El calentamiento**

Sea level – **El nivel del mar**   *Animal species* – **Las especies animales**   *Disappearance* – **La desaparición**

2. Gapped phrases (sections 1 & 2)

a. El **desperdicio** de alimentos: *Food waste*   b. La **especie** humana: *The human species*

c. El **tráfico** aéreo: *Air traffic*   d. La contaminación del **aire** y del **agua**: *Air and water pollution*

e. Los gases de efecto **invernadero**: *Greenhouse gases*   f. La **subida** del nivel del mar: *Sea level rise*

3. Broken words (sections 1-3)

a. Inunda**ciones**   b. Los ga**ses**   c. La pér**dida**   d. Combu**stibles**   e. El ni**vel**   f. La sub**ida**

g. La ca**za**   h. Carret**era**   i. La desa**parición**   j. Aéreo   k. Los ali**mentos**   l. La esc**asez**

4. Faulty translation

a. *To endanger*   b. *Road traffic*   c. √   d. √   e. *To stop*   f. *Hunting*   g. *To threaten*

5. Translate into English (all sections)

a. Transport   b. Hunting   c. Fuels   d. The footprint   e. The greenhouse effect   f. Overconsumption

g. Global warming   h. The species   i. World population   j. To stop   k. The exhaustion   l. To endanger

6. Missing vowels a. La especie b. La caza c. El agotamiento d. Los combustibles e. El sobreconsumo
f. El calentamiento g. La pérdida

7. Anagrams

a. Especies b. Nivel c. Huella d. Agotamiento e. Combustibles f. Deshielo g. Polos h. Calentamiento

8. Sentence puzzle

a. La población mundial no deja de crecer   b. El efecto invernadero se acelera por la actividad humana

c. El calentamiento global se debe a la contaminación   d. El deshielo de los polos provoca inundaciones en las

zonas costeras   e. La extinción de especies animales amenaza la diversidad de la fauna

f. La temperatura de los océanos no para de aumentar cada año

9. Complete the table

Hunting: **Caza**   *Exhaustion:* **Agotamiento**   *Global warming:* **Calentamiento global**   *Fuels:* **Combustibles**

Waste: **Malgasto**   *Melting:* **Deshielo**   *Floods:* **Inundaciones**   *To increase:* **Aumentar**   *Loss:* **Pérdida**

10. Wordsearch

							C		
D	I	V	E	R	S	I	D	A	D
E					N	N	Z		
S				A	U	G	A		
H	U	E	L	L	A	N			
I			F		D				
E		E	R	I	A				
L				C					
O	E	S	P	E	C	I	E	S	
				Ó					
	O	N	I	Ü	G	N	I	P	

Hunting: **Caza**
Diversity: **Diversidad**
Melting: **Deshielo**
Species: **Especies**
Flood: **Inundaciones**
Penguin: **Pingüino**
Water: **Agua**
Air: **Aire**
Footprint: **Huella**
Fauna: **Fauna**

11. Guided translation

a. El deshielo de los polos   b. La extinción de especies animales   c. Los gases de efecto invernadero

d. Dejar una huella   e. El calentamiento global   f. La temperatura de los océanos   g. La población mundial

12. Translate into Spanish

a. El deshielo de los polos   b. La actividad de la especie humana

c. La desaparición de especies animales y vegetales   d. La subida del nivel del mar

e. El calentamiento global es un fenómeno preocupante   f. La contaminación del aire amenaza nuestra salud

g. Las inundaciones son cada vez más frecuentes   h. Hay mucho desperdicio de recursos naturales

i. Dejar una huella en el medio ambiente   j. La caza pone en peligro a muchas especies animales

ANSWERS - UNIT 4 - Test (/100)

1. Vocabulary recognition – Spanish to English translation (/15)

a. The melting of the ice caps

f. To threaten

k. The landscape

b. The factories

g. The fires

l. The shortage

c. The greenhouse effect

h. The drought

m. The floods

d. Waste

i. The extinction

n. The fuels

e. Traffic jams

j. The sea

o. The overconsumption

2. Syntax/Lexicogrammar – Split sentences (/5)

La población mundial no deja	**de crecer**
El deshielo de los polos provoca	**inundaciones**
El efecto invernadero se acelera	**por la actividad humana**
Deberíamos	**prohibir las pesticidas**
Hay que reducir el malgasto	**de los recursos**

3. Grammar/Morphology/Vocabulary – Tangled translation (/20)

a. Los **gases** de escape de **los coches**

g. **E**n las zonas **costeras**

b. La **diversidad** de la **fauna**

h. El d**esperdicio** de **comida**

c. La **extinción** de e**species** vegetales

i. Dejar una h**uella** en el m**edio ambiente**

d. **Hay** muchos a**tascos**

j. La **subida** del n**ivel** del mar

e. El **aumento** de la **población**

k. La **temperatura** de los **océanos**

f. El agotamiento de los **recursos naturales**

l. La **escasez** de a**limentos**

4. Translate into Spanish (/ 60 – each full sentence – 6 points)

a. Los combustibles fósiles contribuyen al efecto invernadero.

b. El deshielo de los polos causa la subida del nivel del mar.

c. Las ballenas azules y los osos polares son especies en peligro.

d. Los atascos son una causa importante de la contaminación del aire.

e. El aumento de la población es la causa principal de la contaminación.

f. La deforestación es una de las causas del calentamiento global.

g. La temperatura de los océanos sigue creciendo cada día.

h. La subida del nivel del mar causa inundaciones en las costas.

i. El efecto invernadero se acelera debido a la contaminación.

j. El agotamiento de los recursos naturales es un gran problema.

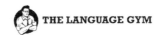

Unit 5. Environment: potential solutions

KEY VOCABULARY - Foundation

1. Las soluciones

Hay que: *We have to*

Debemos: *We must*

-cambiar nuestros hábitos:
change our habits

-cerrar los centros de las ciudades a los coches: *close city centres to cars*

-compartir el coche: *do carpooling*

-comprar productos sostenibles:
buy sustainable products

-evitar los productos de un solo uso:
avoid single-use products

-limitar el uso del agua:
limit the use of water

-plantar árboles: *plant trees*

-preservar los bosques: *preserve forests*

-prohibir los fertilizantes químicos:
to ban chemical fertilisers

-prohibir los pesticidas: *ban pesticides*

-reciclar los desechos: *recycle rubbish*

-reducir el malgasto de recursos:
reduce the waste of resources

-reducir la deforestación:
reduce deforestation

-reducir las actividades contaminantes:
reduce polluting activities

-reducir nuestro consumo:
reduce our consumption

-reutilizar las cosas: *reuse things*

-usar una bicicleta para trayectos cortos:
use a bike for short journeys

-usar/utilizar el transporte público:
use public transport

2. Los problemas

El agotamiento de recursos:
The exhaustion of resources

El efecto invernadero:
The greenhouse effect

El embalaje: *Packaging*

La contaminación del aire / agua / suelo:
Air / water / soil pollution

La extinción de especies:
The extinction of species

La sequía: *Drought*

La subida de temperaturas: *The rise in temperatures*

La superpoblación: *Overpopulation*

1. Match

Plantar	***To limit***
Prohibir	***To plant***
Parar	***To preserve***
Reutilizar	***To ban***
Preservar	***To reduce***
Cambiar	***To buy***
Reducir	***To stop***
Comprar	***To reuse***
Evitar	***To avoid***
Limitar	***To close***
Cerrar	***To change***

2. Broken words

a. Compa_ _ _ _ el coc_ _ :
Carpooling

b. Árb_ _ _ _ : *Trees*

c. Con_ _ _ _ : *Consumption*

d. Bos_ _ _ _ : *Forests*

e. Vi_ _ _ _ : *Journeys*

f. Fertil_ _ _ _ _ _ _ :
Fertilisers

g. Mal_ _ _ _ _ : *Waste*

h. Prod_ _ _ _ _ : *Products*

i. U_ _ _ : *To use*

j. Háb_ _ _ _ : *Habits*

3. Complete the English translations

a. Cerrar los centros de las ciudades: *To _____ the city centres*

b. Plantar árboles: *To plant _____*

c. Utilizar el transporte público: *To use _____*

d. Comprar productos sostenibles: *To ___ sustainable products*

e. Prohibir los fertilizantes químicos: *To ban chemical _____*

f. Cambiar nuestros hábitos: *To change our _____*

g. Limitar el uso del agua: *To limit the use of _____*

h. Compartir el coche: *To do _____*

i. Reciclar los desechos: *To recycle _____*

j. El malgasto de recursos: *The waste of _____*

4. Sentence puzzle

a. Debemos reducir el recursos de malgasto
We must reduce the waste of resources

b. químicos que prohibir Hay los fertilizantes
We have to ban chemical fertilisers

c. los que prohibir Hay pesticidas
We have to ban pesticides

d. Debemos los desechos reciclar
We must recycle rubbish

e. nuestro reducir consumo Debemos
We must reduce our consumption

f. Debemos bicicleta usar una para trayectos cortos
We must use a bike for short journeys

g. nuestras que costumbres Tenemos cambiar
We have to change our habits

 THE LANGUAGE GYM

5. Choose the correct translation

a. Los combustibles: *fuels / droughts / gases*

b. El aumento: *reduction / vegetation / increase*

c. El sobreconsumo: *overcrowding / overconsumption / overuse*

d. Los atascos: *bottles / glass wasting / traffic jams*

e. El embalaje: *cigarette butts / gases / packaging*

f. La caza: *hunting / fishing / waste*

g. La contaminación del suelo: *air pollution /evil worms/ soil pollution*

h. El agotamiento: *waste / exhaustion / rise*

i. La sequía: *waste / drought / fishing*

j. La superpoblación: *exhaustion / overpopulation / overconsumption*

6. Missing letters challenge

a. La ca_a

b. L_s comb_stibl_s

c. La seq _ _a

d. L_ sup_ _ pobla_ón

e. L_s at_sc_s

f. El au_ _nto

g. E_ mal_a_to

h. Los ga_e_

i. Las cos_umb_es

j. E_ em_ala_e

7. Break the flow

a. Debemoscambiarnuestroshábitos

b. Debemosplantarárboles

c. Debemospreservarlosbosques

d. Debemosreducirladeforestación

e. Hayquecompartirelcoche

f. Hayquelimitarelusodelagua

g. Hayquereducirnuestroconsumo

9. Translate into Spanish

a. Animal species

b. Public transport

c. The waste of resources

d. Chemical fertilisers

e. The rise in temperatures

f. Exhaustion

g. Rubbish

h. Trees

i. Hunting

10. Complete with a suitable word

a. Reciclar los _____

b. Reducir el _____ de recursos

c. Reutilizar ___ _____

d. Cambiar nuestras _____

e. Plantar _____

f. Evitar productos de un solo _____

g. Utilizar _____ para los trayectos cortos

8. Complete with the correct option

a. Hay que limitar el _____ de recursos naturales

b. Hay que _____ el agua de lluvia para regar

c. Hay que plantar más _____

d. Hay que _____ el coche siempre que sea posible

e. Debería usar una bicicleta para los trayectos _____

f. Hay que utilizar el transporte _____

g. Hay que limitar el consumo de _____

h. Hay que reciclar los _____

i. La caza furtiva amenaza a las _____ en peligro

j. Tenemos que _____ nuestras costumbres

público	compartir	especies	cortos	cambiar
desechos	malgasto	árboles	recursos	recoger

11. Translate into Spanish

a. It is necessary to reduce the waste of natural resources

b. We must use public transport

c. We must ban the use of chemical fertilisers

d. It is necessary to plant more trees

e. It is better to use a bike for short journeys

f. We must recycle rubbish and reuse things

g. We must limit the consumption of water

h. We have to change our habits

 THE LANGUAGE GYM

KEY VOCABULARY - Higher

Los objetivos (*the aims*)

Para combatir la contaminación del aire:
To combat air pollution

Para evitar la sequía:
To avoid droughts

Para ralentizar el aumento de las temperaturas:
To slow down the rise of temperature

Para limitar el consumo excesivo:
To limit overconsumption

Para luchar contra la contaminación:
To fight against pollution

Para reducir la deforestación:
To reduce deforestation

Para preservar la Tierra:
To preserve the Earth

Para proteger a los animales:
To protect animals

Para proteger el medio ambiente:
To protect the environment

Para proteger las plantas: *To protect plants*

Para ralentizar el agotamiento de los recursos:
To slow down the exhaustion of resources

Para reducir el desperdicio de recursos:
To reduce the wasting of resources

Para salvar nuestro planeta:
To save our planet

Las soluciones

Hay que: *We have to*
Deberíamos: *We should*

-evitar los productos de un solo uso:
avoid single-use products

-cambiar el comportamiento de las personas:
change people's behaviour

-limitar el uso de agua potable:
limit the use of drinkable water

-plantar árboles: *plant trees*

-reciclar los desechos: *recycle rubbish*

-recoger el agua de lluvia: *collect rainwater*

-reducir las actividades contaminantes:
reduce polluting activities

-reducir nuestro consumo de agua:
reduce our water consumption

-reutilizar las cosas: *reuse objects*

Hay que prohibir: *We have to ban*

-la caza de especies en peligro de extinción:
the hunting of endangered species

-la caza furtiva: *poaching*

-la colecta de flores silvestres:
the picking of wild flowers

-los pesticidas: *pesticides*

1. Match

Para ralentizar	*In order to reduce*
Para proteger	*We have to limit*
Para preservar	*In order to save*
Para reducir	*In order to avoid*
Para ahorrar	*In order to fight against*
Para evitar	*We have to plant*
Para luchar contra	*In order to preserve*
Hay que limitar	*We have to ban*
Hay que prohibir	*In order to slow down*
Hay que cambiar	*In order to protect*
Hay que plantar	*We have to change*

2. Gapped translation

a. Para proteger a los animales debemos prohibir la caza de especies en peligro de extinción.
In order to protect the animals it is _____ to ban the _____ of _____ species.

b. Para luchar contra la contaminación del aire debemos reducir las actividades contaminantes, como usar el coche.
In order to _____ air pollution, it is _____ to reduce polluting activities, such as using the _____.

c. Para reducir el malgasto de recursos y materiales debemos reciclar los desechos.
In order to reduce the _____ of resources and materials, we _____ recycle _____.

d. Para proteger las plantas es necesario prohibir la colecta de flores silvestres.
In order to _____ the plants, it is necessary to _____ the picking of _____ flowers.

3. Missing vowels

a. Pr_h_b_r : *To ban*

b. Pl_nt_s : *Plants*

c. C_l_ct_ : *Picking*

d. _rb_l_s : *Trees*

e. C_s_s : *Things*

f. _s_r : *Use*

g. L_ _c_z_ : *Hunting*

h. C_s_s: *Things*

i. S_lv_r: *To save*

j. L_ch_r: *To fight*

4. Broken words

a. Tie____ : *Earth*

b. Rec____ : *To recycle*

c. Pla___ : *To plant*

d. Limi____ : *To limit*

e. Ár____ : *Trees*

f. Ral_____ : *Slow down*

g. Sa_____ : *To save*

h. Col____ : *Picking*

i. Ag_____ : *Water*

j. Pot____ : *Drinkable*

 **THE LANGUAGE GYM**

5. Choose the correct translation

a. Los desechos: *Objects / Waste / Trees*

b. La colecta: *Picking / Landscape/ Earth*

c. Los árboles: *Trees / Flowers / Forests*

d. Potable: *Rain / Drinkable / Disposable*

e. La lluvia: *Species / Rain / Weather*

f. La subida: *Rise / Decline / Waste*

6. Complete with the correct option from the box

a. _____ árboles

b. La _____ de las temperaturas

c. Hay _____ prohibir

d. El agua _____

e. Reciclar los _____

f. Las _____ silvestres

flores
subida
desechos
que
plantar
potable

7. Anagrams

a. dabiSu: *Rise*

b. lesorÁb: *Trees*

c. Rideruc: *To reduce*

d. biPirroh: *To forbid*

e. aL ierTra: *The Earth*

f. saCos: *Things*

g. Ralzarenti: *To slow down*

h. soquBes: *Forests*

8. Sentence puzzle

a. prohibir las Hay que pesticidas:

b. la caza prohibir furtiva Debemos:

c. Podemos más árboles plantar:

d. el uso que limitar de agua Hay potable:

e. Hay cosas reutilizar que las:

9. Complete the table

English	Español
The rise	
	Debemos comprar
	El comportamiento
Single–use products	
	El malgasto
To plant trees	
	El sobreconsumo
We have to	
Soil pollution	

10. Wordsearch: Find the Spanish for the listed words

R	A	T	S	A	G	L	A	M
I	M	Á	N	E	M	S	N	E
P	A	R	A	R	A	R	I	D
E	U	B	S	A	R	A	C	E
P	R	O	D	U	C	T	O	S
E	I	L	A	S	M	A	L	E
N	T	E	Z	O	A	S	E	C
R	G	S	A	T	V	I	C	H
Ü	M	A	C	G	A	S	T	O
G	I	U	A	M	I	D	A	S
N	O	R	L	N	T	R	U	F

Products: P

Trees: A

I use: U

Picking: C

Rubbish: D

To waste: M

To stop: P

Hunting: C

11. Guided translation

a. L__ s_____ : *The rise*

b. E__ m_____ d__ r_____ :
The waste of resources

c. E__ a___ p_____ : *Drinkable water*

d. L__ p_____ : *The products*

e. L_ c_____ f_____ : *Poaching*

f. L_____ c_____ : *To fight against*

g. P_____ : *To ban*

h. P____ r_____ : *In order to reduce*

i. R_____ e__ a_____ d__ l_____ :
To collect rainwater

j. E__ c_____ d__ l_ g_____ :
The behaviour of people

12. Translate into Spanish

a. In order to reduce deforestation

b. We must buy sustainable products

c. We have to to avoid single-use products

d. In order to limit overconsumption

e. The pollution of the air and of the soil

f. In order to reduce the waste of resources

g. We must recycle rubbish and reuse things

h. It is necessary to limit the use of drinkable water

i. We must collect rainwater

j. It is important to preserve the forests

UNIT 5 - Test (/100)

1. Vocabulary recognition - Spanish to English translation (/15)

a. Los productos sostenibles

b. Los desechos

c. Las costumbres

d. El consumo

e. Cerrar

f. Hay que

g. Contaminante

h. Los fertilizantes

i. Los árboles

j. Evitar

k. Compartir el coche

l. Debemos

m. Prohibir

n. Malgastar

o. Químicos

2. Syntax/Lexicogrammar – Split sentences (/5)

Hay que usar la bicicleta para	**el coche para ir al colegio**
Debemos evitar los productos	**reciclar los desechos**
Debemos	**trayectos cortos**
Hay que compartir	**los bosques**
Debemos preservar	**de un solo uso**

3. Grammar/Morphology/Vocabulary – Tangled translation (/20)

a. Los gases de **exhaust** de los **cars**

b. **We must share** el coche

c. La **extinction** de **species** animales

d. Los **products** de un **single** uso

e. **To buy** productos **sustainable**

f. **To recycle** los **waste** industriales

g. **To change** nuestras **habits**

h. Prohibir los **fertilizers chemical**

i. **To ban** la **hunting** furtiva

j. El **exhaustion** de los **resources**

k. **To slow down** nuestro **consumption**

l. **To reduce** las **activities** contaminantes

4. Translate into Spanish (/ 60 – each full sentence = 6 points)

a. We must use a bike or walk for short journeys.

b. We have to recycle rubbish and reuse things.

c. It is important to limit our use of drinkable water.

d. We must reduce polluting activities and preserve the forests.

e. We have to avoid single-use products.

f. We should ban the use of pesticides and chemical fertilizers.

g. We must limit overconsumption of resources.

h. Deforestation causes the extinction of animal species.

i. We must change our habits drastically (*drásticamente*). It is very important.

j. We have to reduce the consumption and use of energy.

 **THE LANGUAGE GYM**

ANSWERS - Unit 5. Environment: potential solutions - Foundation

1. Match

Plantar – *To plant*   Prohibir – *To ban*   Parar – *To stop*   Reutilizar – *To reuse*   Preservar – *To preserve*
Cambiar – *To change*   Reducir – *To reduce*   Comprar – *To buy*   Evitar – *To avoid*
Limitar – *To limit*   Cerrar – *To close*

2. Broken words

a. Compa**rtir** el coc**he**   b. Árb**oles**   c. Con**sumo**   d. Bos**ques**   e. Vi**ajes**   f. Ferti**lizantes**
g. Mal**gasto**   h. Prod**uctos**   i. U**sar**   j. Háb**itos**

3. Complete the English translations

a. close   b. trees   c. public transport   d. buy   e. fertilisers   f. habits   g. water   h. carpooling   i. rubbish
j. resources

4. Sentence puzzle

a. Debemos reducir el malgasto de recursos   b. Hay que prohibir los fertilizantes químicos
c. Hay que prohibir los pesticidas   d. Debemos reciclar los desechos
e. Debemos reducir nuestro consumo   f. Debemos usar una bicicleta para trayectos cortos g. Tenemos que cambiar nuestras costumbres

5. Choose the correct translation

a. fuels   b. increase   c. overconsumption   d. traffic jams   e. packaging   f. hunting   g. soil pollution
h. exhaustion   i. drought   j. overpopulation

6. Missing letters challenge

a. La caza   b. Los combustibles   c. La sequía   d. La superpoblación   e. Los atascos
f. El aumento   g. El malgasto   h. Los gases   i. Las costumbres   j. El embalaje

7. Break the flow

a. Debemos cambiar nuestros hábitos   b. Debemos plantar árboles   c. Debemos preservar los bosques
d. Debemos reducir la deforestación   e. Hay que compartir el coche   f. Hay que limitar el uso del agua
g. Hay que reducir nuestro consumo

8. Complete with the correct option

a. Hay que limitar el malgasto de recursos naturales   b. Hay que recoger el agua de lluvia para regar
c. Hay que plantar más árboles   d. Hay que compartir el coche siempre que sea posible
e. Debería usar una bicicleta para los trayectos cortos   f. Hay que utilizar el transporte público
g. Hay que limitar el consumo de recursos   h. Hay que reciclar los desechos
i. La caza furtiva amenaza a las especies en peligro   j. Tenemos que cambiar nuestras costumbres

9. Translate into Spanish

a. Las especies animales   b. El transporte público   c. El malgasto de recursos
d. Los fertilizantes químicos   e. La subida de temperaturas   f. El agotamiento   g. Los desechos
h. Los árboles   i. La caza

10. Complete with a suitable word

a. desechos   b. malgasto   c. los productos/las cosas   d. costumbres   e. árboles   f. uso   g. la bicicleta

11. Translate into Spanish

a. Hay que reducir el malgasto de recursos naturales   b. Debemos usar el transporte público
c. Debemos prohibir el uso de fertilizantes químicos   d. Hay que plantar más árboles
e. Es mejor usar la bicicleta para trayectos cortos   f. Debemos reciclar los residuos y reutilizar las cosas
g. Debemos limitar el consumo de agua   h. Tenemos que cambiar nuestras costumbres

ANSWERS - Unit 5. Environment: potential solutions - Higher

1. Match

Para ralentizar – *In order to slow down*   Para proteger – *In order to protect*
Para preservar – *In order to preserve*   Para reducir – *In order to reduce*   Para ahorrar – *In order to save*
Para evitar – *In order to avoid*   Para luchar contra – *In order to fight against*
Hay que limitar – *We have to limit* Hay que prohibir – *We have to ban*   Hay que cambiar – *We have to change*
Hay que plantar – *We have to plant*

2. Gapped translation

a. necessary / hunting / endangered   b. combat / reduce / car   c. waste / must / rubbish
d. protect / forbid / wild

3. Missing vowels

a. Prohibir   b. Plantas   c. Colecta   d. Árboles   e. Cosas   f. Usar   g. La caza   h. Cosas   i. Salvar   j. Luchar

4. Broken words

a. Tie**rra**   b. Rec**icl**ar   c. Pla**nt**ar   d. Lim**itar**   e. Árboles   f. Rale**ntizar**   g. Sal**var**   h. Col**ecta**   i. Ag**ua**
j. Pot**able**

5. Choose the correct translation

a. *waste*   b. *picking*   c. *trees*   d. *drinkable*   e. *rain*   f. *rise*

6. Complete with the correct option from the box

a. plantar   b. subida   c. que   d. potable   e. desechos   f. flores

7. Anagrams

a. Subida   b. Árboles   c. Reducir   d. Prohibir   e. La Tierra   f. Cosas   g. Ralentizar   h. Bosques

8. Sentence puzzle

a. Hay que prohibir las pesticidas   b. Debemos prohibir la caza furtiva   c. Podemos plantar más árboles
d. Hay que limitar el uso de agua potable   e. Hay que reutilizar las cosas

9. Complete the table

The rise: **La subida**   *We must buy:* **Debemos comprar**   *Behaviour:* **El comportamiento**
Single–use products: **Productos de un solo uso**   *Waste:* **El malgasto**   *To plant trees:* **Plantar árboles**
Overconsumption: **El sobreconsumo**   *We have to:* **Hay que**   *Soil pollution:* **La contaminación del suelo**

10. Wordsearch

R	A	T	S	A	G	L	A	M
	Á							
P	A	R	A	R				D
	B						C	E
P	R	O	D	U	C	T	O	S
	L	A	S				L	E
	E	Z	O				E	C
	S	A					C	H
	C						T	O
	A						A	S
	L							

Products: **Productos**
Trees: **Árboles**
I use: **Uso**
Picking: **Colecta**
Rubbish: **Desechos**
To waste: **Malgastar**
To stop: **Parar**
Hunting: **Caza**

11. Guided translation

a. La subida   b. El malgasto de recursos   c. El agua potable   d. Los productos   e. La caza furtiva
f. Luchar contra   g. Prohibir   h. Para reducir   i. Recoger el agua de lluvia
j. El comportamiento de la gente

12. Translate into Spanish

a. Para reducir la deforestación   b. Debemos comprar productos sostenibles
c. Hay que evitar los productos de un solo uso   d. Para limitar el sobreconsumo (o consumo excesivo)
e. La contaminación del aire y del suelo   f. Para reducir el malgasto de recursos
g. Debemos reciclar la basura y reutilizar las cosas   h. Es necesario limitar el uso de agua potable
i. Debemos recoger agua de lluvia   j. Es importante preservar los bosques

 THE LANGUAGE GYM

ANSWERS - UNIT 5 - Test (/100)

1. Vocabulary recognition – Spanish to English translation (/15)

a. Sustainable products	f. It is necessary to	k. Carpooling
b. Waste	g. Polluting	l. We must
c. Habits	h. Fertilisers	m. To ban
d. Consumption	i. Trees	n. To waste
e. To close	j. To avoid	o. Chemical

2. Syntax/Lexicogrammar – Split sentences (/5)

Hay que usar la bicicleta para	**trayectos cortos**
Debemos evitar los productos	**de un solo uso**
Debemos	**reciclar los desechos**
Hay que compartir	**el coche para ir al colegio**
Debemos preservar	**los bosques**

3. Grammar/Morphology/Vocabulary – Tangled translation (/20)

a. Los gases de **escape** de los **coches**

b. **Debemos compartir** el coche

c. La **extinción** de las **especies** animales

d. Los **productos** de un **solo** uso

e. **Comprar** productos **sostenibles**

f. **Reciclar** los **desechos** industriales

g. **Cambiar** nuestras **costumbres**

h. Prohibir los **fertilizantes químicos**

i. **Prohibir** la **caza** furtiva

j. El **agotamiento** de los **recursos**

k. **Ralentizar** nuestro **consumo**

l. **Reducir** las **actividades** contaminantes

4. Translate into Spanish (/ 60 – each full sentence – 6 points)

a. Debemos usar la bicicleta o andar/caminar para trayectos cortos.

b. Hay que reciclar la basura y reutilizar las cosas.

c. Es importante limitar nuestro uso de agua potable.

d. Debemos reducir las actividades contaminantes y preservar los bosques.

e. Hay que evitar los productos de un solo uso.

f. Deberíamos prohibir el uso de pesticidas y fertilizantes químicos.

g. Debemos limitar el consumo excesivo de recursos.

h. La deforestación causa la extinción de especies animales.

i. Debemos cambiar nuestras costumbres drásticamente. Es muy importante.

j. Hay que reducir el consumo y uso de energía.

Unit 6. What I study, what I like/dislike and why

KEY VOCABULARY - Foundation

1. Hablar de las asignaturas

Aprendo: *I learn*
Estudio: *I study*
Me encanta: *I love*
Odio: *I hate*
Prefiero: *I prefer*
-las lenguas extranjeras: *foreign languages*
-las asignaturas de ciencias: *science subjects*
Mi asignatura favorita es:
My favourite subject is
-el alemán: *German*
-el arte: *art*
-el español: *Spanish*
-el inglés: *English*
-el teatro: *drama*
-la historia: *history*
-la informática: *IT*
-la química: *chemistry*

2. Decir lo que (no) me gusta

Ya que es: *As it's*
-aburrido: *boring*
-difícil: *difficult*
-emocionante: *exciting*
-enriquecedor: *enriching*
-entretenido: *entertaining*
-fácil: *easy*
-fascinante: *fascinating*
-útil: *useful*
Ya que el/la profe es: *As the teacher is*
-divertido/a: *funny*
-gracioso/a: *funny*
-motivador/a: *motivating*
-simpático/a: *nice*
-trabajador/a: *hardworking*
Ya que el/la profe: *As the teacher*
-tiene un buen/mal sentido del humor:
has a good/bad sense of humour
-explica bien: *explains well*
-(no) me ayuda mucho:
(doesn't) help(s) me a lot
-nunca se enfada: *never gets angry*

3. Verbos importantes

Aprender: *To learn*
Aprobar (un examen): *To pass (an exam)*
Estudiar: *To study*
Hacer un examen: *To do/take an exam*

1. Match

Aprendo	*I understand*
Las lenguas extranjeras	*I learn*
Ella explica bien	*Subject*
Entiendo	*It's exciting*
Es entretenido	*Foreign languages*
Tomo (un examen)	*I take (an exam)*
La asignatura	*It's easy*
Es emocionante	*She explains well*
Estudio	*Useful*
Es fácil	*ICT*
La informática	*It's entertaining*
Es útil	*I study*

2. Complete the words

a. *Motivating*: Moti_ _ _ _ _
b. *Funny*: _ _ _cioso
c. *Easy*: Fá_ _ _
d. *Chemistry*: La quí_ _ _ _
e. *History*: La hist_ _ _ _
f. *A subject*: Una asigna_ _ _ _
g. *He explains*: Él exp_ _ _ _
h. *To do (an exam)*: Ha_ _ _
i. *Difficult*: Difí_ _ _
j. *Fascinating*: Fascin_ _ _ _

3. Anagrams (section 2)

a. itÚl
b. tivorModa
c. dorAburi
d. pasAonatein
e. darbelAra
f. doverDiti
g. soGacrio
h. cilFá
i. fíDicil
j. teInsarente

4. Translate into English

a. Es creativo
b. El profe es simpático
c. Es fácil
d. Me encanta el arte
e. Es aburrido
f. Me gusta la historia
g. Es útil
h. Me gusta la química
i. La profe me ayuda
j. Es entretenido
k. Nunca se enfada
l. Es trabajadora

5. Spot and correct the wrong English translations

a. Entretenido: *Easy*
b. Motivador: *Motivating*
c. Aburrido: *Boring*
d. Emocionante: *Entertaining*
e. Gracioso: *Funny*
f. Útil: *Enriching*
g. Simpático: *Nice*
h. Trabajador: *Lazy*
i. Inútil: *Useful*
j. Fácil: *Easy*

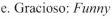 

THE LANGUAGE GYM

6. Gapped translation

a. Me encanta el español porque es e_____: *I love Spanish because it is exciting*

b. H__ e_____ el inglés desde hace cinco años: *I have studied English for five years*

c. Mi _____ favorita es la informática porque es _____:
My favourite subject is ICT because it is useful

d. En el colegio, _____ dos _____ extranjeras: *At school, I learn two foreign languages*

e. El año próximo, voy a _____ mis _____ de GCSE:
Next year, I am going to take my GCSE exams

f. Mi profesora de español es de San Roque y _____ un buen _____ del humor:
My Spanish teacher is from San Roque and she has a good sense of humour

g. Mi profe _____ ciencias es muy _____: *My science teacher is very hard-working*

h. _____ profe de matemáticas no se _____ nunca: *My maths teacher never gets angry*

7. Missing vowels

a. _ntr_t_n_d_ *Entertaining*
b. _m_c__n_nt_ *Exciting*
c. _n_t_l *Useless*
d. _t_l *Useful*
e. M_t_v_d_r *Motivating*
f. S_mp_t_c_ *Nice*
g. _b_rr_d_ *Boring*
h. Gr_c__s_ *Funny*
i. F_c_l *Easy*
j. Tr_b_j_d_r *Hard-working*

8. Wordsearch – Find the Spanish for the listed words

P	I	N	G	Ü	I	N	O	M	O
R	O	D	A	V	I	T	O	M	D
O	O	E	U	N	G	E	R	O	I
F	U	D	O	L	I	L	C	O	R
E	L	R	A	N	R	I	L	S	R
N	I	S	F	J	T	F	P	O	U
R	T	N	U	Á	A	N	S	I	B
E	Ú	I	P	M	C	B	O	C	A
P	N	M	O	S	P	I	A	A	D
F	I	D	E	D	N	C	L	R	E
S	A	U	G	N	E	L	I	G	T

Nice: S
Hard-working: T
Boring: A
Useless: I
Easy: F
Funny: G
Motivating: M
Teacher: P
Languages: L

9. Translate into Spanish

a. It's creative

b. The teacher is friendly

c. It's easy

d. I love art

e. It's boring

f. I like maths

g. It is difficult

h. I like history a lot

i. The teacher helps me

j. It's entertaining

k. She never gets angry

l. She is hard working

10. Translate into Spanish

a. I like P.E. because the teacher is fun and friendly

b. I don't like maths because it's boring

c. At school I learn two languages: French and German

d. My history teacher is very good. He explains things well

e. My English teacher helps me when I have a problem

f. My science teacher has a good sense of humour

g. My favourite subject is foreign languages

h. I love Spanish because it is exciting and useful

THE LANGUAGE GYM

KEY VOCABULARY Higher

1. Lo que estudio (*What I study*)

Aprendo: *I learn* / Estudio: *I study*

-informática: *IT*

-química: *chemistry*

-lenguas extranjeras: *foreign languages*

-teatro: *drama*

2. Las asignaturas que más me gustan (+)

A mi parecer, la mejor asignatura es el arte:
According to me, the best subject is art

Lo que más me gusta estudiar son las matemáticas:
What I like studying the most is maths

Mi clase favorita es la biología:
My favourite lesson is biology

3. Las asignaturas que menos me gustan (-)

No obstante: *Nonetheless*

-lo que no soporto: *what I can't stand*

-lo que menos me gusta estudiar:
what I like studying the least is

4. Por qué (no) me gustan las asignaturas

Me encanta esta asignatura porque:
I love this subject because

Odio esta asignatura porque:
I hate this subject because

-es fácil / difícil: *easy / hard*

-es fascinante / aburrida: *fascinating / boring*

-es motivadora / desmotivadora: *(de)motivating*

-es útil / inútil: *useful / useless*

-la encuentro fácil / difícil *I find it easy / hard*

-me muero de aburrimiento: *boring to death*

Además, el/la profe es:
Moreover, the teacher is

-divertido/a /aburrido/a *fun/boring*

-paciente/impaciente: *patient/impatient*

-simpático/a / antipático/a: *nice/unfriendly*

-trabajador/a / perezoso/a: *hardworking/lazy*

Tiene buen/mal sentido del humor:
He/She has a good/bad sense of humour

Y él/ella: *And he/she*

-explica las cosas bien/mal:
explains things well/badly

-enseña bien/mal: *teaches well/badly*

-(no) me ayuda: *helps/doesn't help me*

-nos da muchos/pocos deberes:
gives us a lot of/not much homework

-se enfada fácilmente/nunca se enfada:
gets angry easily/never gets angry

Finalmente, durante las clases:
Finally, during the lessons:

-aprendo mucho / no aprendo nada:
I learn a lot / I don't learn anything

-(no) entiendo: *I (don't) understand*

1. Match (sections 1–3)

Aprendo	*It's art*
Estudio	*What I hate*
Lo que me gusta estudiar	*However*
Mi clase favorita	*Foreign languages*
Es la química	*I learn*
Sin embargo	*It's IT*
Lo que odio	*What I don't like*
Es la informática	*My favourite lesson*
Las lenguas extranjeras	*I study*
Lo que no me gusta	*It's chemistry*
Es el dibujo	*What I enjoy studying*

2. Gapped translation (sections 2–4)

a. Lo que me gusta estudiar: *What I enjoy* _____

b. Mi clase favorita: *My favourite* _____

c. La mejor asignatura: *The* _____ *subject*

d. Lo que no soporto: *What I* _____

e. A mi parecer: _____ *to me*

f. Me parece difícil: *I* _____ *it difficult*

g. Me muero de aburrimiento: *It is boring to* _____

h. Tiene un buen sentido del humor: *He has a*
_____ *sense of humour*

i. Ella es divertida: *She is* _____

3. Translate into English (sections 2–4)

a. Esta asignatura

b. Es fascinante

c. A mi parecer, es útil

d. Un buen sentido del humor

e. Me muero de aburrimiento

f. Es divertido

g. Ella es trabajadora

h. La encuentro fácil

i. Aprendo mucho

4. Broken words (section 4)

a. Asig_____ : *Subject*

b. Ad_____ : *Moreover*

c. Deb____ : *Homework*

d. Dif_____ : *Hard*

e. Út____ : *Useful*

f. Bi____ : *Well*

g. Ma___ : *Badly*

5. Missing vowels (section 4)

a. D_v_rt_d_

b. F_c_l

c. D_f_c_l

d. B__n

e. M_l

f. Tr_b_j_d_r

g. P_r_z_s_

THE LANGUAGE GYM

6. Choose the correct translation

a. Aprendo: *I learn / I study / I read*

b. Aburrido: *Fun / Exciting / Boring*

c. Divertido: *Boring / Rubbish / Fun*

d. Informática: *Maths / Art / IT*

e. Fácil: *Fun / Hard / Easy*

f. Difícil: *Hard /Easy / Fun*

7. Complete with the correct option from the box

a. Aprendo _____ extranjeras

b. Lo que más me _____

c. Mi _____ favorita

d. Me _____ demasiado difícil

e. No _____ nada

f. Aprendo _____ en las clases

gusta
entiendo
lenguas
mucho
parece
asignatura

8. Match the opposites

Aburrido	*Más*
Fácil	*Perezoso*
Bueno	*Divertido*
Bien	*Mal*
Menos	*Difícil*
Paciente	*Malo*
Trabajador	*Impaciente*

9. Gapped English to Spanish translation

a. La asignatura _____ _____ me gusta : *The subject I like the most*

b. Tiene un ____ sentido del _____ : *He has a good sense of humour*

c. Ella es _____ y _____ : *She is hard-working and nice*

d. Nos _____ demasiados _____ : *He gives us too much homework*

e. Ella _____ me _____ : *She never helps me*

f. Él _____ bien las _____ : *He explains things well*

g. _____ mucho en las _____ : *I learn a lot in the lessons*

10. Complete the table

English	Español
I learn	
	Entiendo
I find	
He gives	
	No se enfada
	Enseña
He explains	
	Estudio
What I like	

11. Wordsearch – Find the Spanish for the listed words

U	M	Q	U	N	S	Ñ	E
R	A	Ñ	E	S	N	E	S
O	L	A	M	O	E	S	P
R	I	R	S	E	R	T	A
T	P	D	A	M	N	U	Ñ
N	A	P	R	E	N	D	O
E	B	A	I	G	Ñ	I	L
U	Z	B	N	U	P	O	G
C	N	I	A	S	N	G	N
N	A	D	N	T	I	Ü	I
E	M	Y	S	A	R	E	P

I study: E

He teaches: E

He gives us: N

I find: E

I learn: A

I like: M

Spanish: E

Badly: M

Well: B

12. Guided translation

a. *He explains well*: E_____ b_____

b. *I find this hard*: L_ e_____ d_____

c. *I don't understand*: N_ e_____

d. *What I like the most*: L_ q___ m__ m_ g_____

e. *I study science*: E_____ c_____

f. *He gives us homework*: N___ d__ d_____

g. *He gets angry easily*: S_ e_____ f_____

h. *My favourite lesson*: M_ c_____ f_____

i. *I don't learn anything*: N_ a_____ n_____

j. *I love IT*: M_ e_____ l_ i_____

k. *He teaches very badly*: E_____ m____ m_____

13. Translate into Spanish

a. At school I study maths, chemistry, two foreign languages, art, English, history and P.E.

b. The school subjects I like the most are English and Spanish

c. I like Spanish because the teacher is fun, the lessons are fun and I learn a lot

d. What I can't stand is maths because I find it difficult and the teacher explains things badly

e. My English teacher gives us too much homework and gets angry very easily

f. In the chemistry lessons, I don't understand much. However, in the maths lessons I learn a lot

UNIT 6 - Test (/100)

1. Vocabulary recognition - Spanish to English translation (/15)

a. La informática

b. Una asignatura

c. Aprendo

d. El arte

e. Perezoso

f. Fácil

g. Porque

h. Divertido

i. Bueno

j. Malo

k. Trabajador

l. Se enfada

m. Emocionante

n. Estudiar

o. El alemán

2. Syntax/Lexicogrammar – Split sentences (/5)

Yo pienso que esta	**desde hace un año**
La biologia	**emocionante y motivador**
Estudio alemán y francés	**asignatura es muy interesante**
Lo encuentro	**es muy aburrida**
Sin embargo, lo que	**no me gusta es la historia**

3. Grammar/Morphology/Vocabulary – Tangled translation (/20)

a. **What** prefiero **to study**

b. **It's** muy **boring**

c. Es **useless** en la **life**

d. El profe **gives** muchos **homework**

e. Es **too** complicado

f. **According to me**, es relajante

g. Lo **find** bastante **easy**

h. Me encanta el **Spanish**

i. Tiene un buen **sense** del humor

j. Lo que yo no **stand**, es la química

k. **I hate** esta **subject**

l. Mi **class** favorita, es el **art**

4. Translate into Spanish (/ 60 – each full sentence = 6 points)

a. I like this school subject because it's exciting and motivating.

b. Finally, what I hate is chemistry, because it's boring.

c. I can't stand art, because I think it is useless in life.

d. What I like to study the most is music.

e. I don't like German, because it is too hard.

f. Nonetheless, maths is really useful.

g. I like geography, but I don't like drama.

h. What I truly hate is to take an exam.

i. I quite like Spanish because I find it easy and fun.

j. I have studied music and art since five years ago.

 THE LANGUAGE GYM

ANSWERS - Unit 6. What I study, what I like/dislike and why - Foundation

1. Match

Aprendo – *I learn*   Las lenguas extranjeras – *Foreign languages*   Ella explica bien – *She explains well*
Entiendo – *I understand*   Es entretenido – *It's entertaining*   Tomo (un examen) – *I take (an exam)*
La asignatura – *Subject*   Es emocionante – *It's exciting*   Estudio – *I study*   Es fácil – *It's easy*
La informática – *IT*   Útil – *Useful*

2. Complete the words

a. Moti**vador**   b. **Gra**cioso   c. Fá**cil**   d. La quí**mica**   e. La hist**oria**   f. Una asigna**tura**   g. Él exp**lica**
h. Ha**cer**   i. Dif**ícil**   j. Fascin**ante**

3. Anagrams (section 2)

a. Útil   b. Motivador   c. Aburrido   d. Emocionante   e. Simpático   f. Divertido   g. Gracioso   h. Fácil
i. Difícil   j. Interesante

4. Translate into English

a. It's creative   b. The teacher is nice   c. It's easy   d. I love art   e. It's boring   f. I like history
g. It's useful   h. I like chemistry   i. The teacher helps me   j. It's entertaining   k. He/she never gets angry
l. She is hard-working

5. Spot and correct the wrong English translations

a. √   b. Motivador: *Motivating*   c. Aburrido: *Boring*   d. √   e. Gracioso: *Funny*   f. √   g. Simpático: *Nice*
h. √   i. √   j. Fácil: *Easy*

6. Gapped translation

a. emocionante   b. He estudiado   c. asignatura / útil   d. aprendo / lenguas   e. tomar/hacer / exámenes
f. tiene / sentido   g. de / trabajador   h. Mi / enfada

7. Missing vowels

a. **Entretenido**   b. **Emocionante**   c. **Inútil**   d. **Útil**   e. **Motivador**
f. **Simpático**   g. **Aburrido**   h. **Gracioso**   i. **Fácil**   j. **Trabajador**

8. Wordsearch

P									O
R	O	D	A	V	I	T	O	M	D
O	O							O	I
F		D				C	O	R	
E	L		A		I		S	R	
	I		F	J	T		O	U	
	T		Á	A			I	B	
	Ú		P		C	B		C	A
	N	M			I	A	A		
	I				L	R			
S	A	U	G	N	E	L		G	T

Nice: **Simpático**
Hard-working: **Trabajador**
Boring: **Aburrido**
Useless: **Inútil**
Easy: **Fácil**
Funny: **Gracioso**
Motivating: **Motivador**
Teacher: **Profesor**
Languages: **Lenguas**

9. Translate into Spanish

a. Es creativo   b. El profesor es agradable   c. Es fácil   d. Me encanta el arte   e. Es aburrido
f. Me gustan las matemáticas   g. Es difícil   h. Me gusta mucho la historia   i. La profesora me ayuda
j. Es entretenido   k. Ella nunca se enfada   l. Ella es trabajadora

10. Translate into Spanish

a. Me gusta la gimnasia porque el profesor es divertido y agradable
b. No me gustan las matemáticas porque es aburrido
c. En la escuela estudio dos lenguas: francés y alemán
d. Mi profesor de historia es muy bueno. Explica las cosas muy bien
e. Mi profesora de inglés me ayuda cuando tengo un problema
f. Mi profesora de ciencias tiene un buen sentido del humor
g. Mi asignatura favorita son las lenguas extranjeras
h. Me encanta el español porque es excitante y útil

ANSWERS - Unit 6. What I study, what I like/dislike and why - Higher

1. Match (sections 1–3)
Aprendo – *I learn*   Estudio – *I study*   Lo que me gusta estudiar – *What I like studying*
Mi clase favorita – *My favourite lesson*   Es la química – *It's chemistry*   Sin embargo – *However*
Lo que odio – *What I hate*   Es la informática – *It's IT*   Las lenguas extranjeras – *Foreign languages*
Lo que no me gusta – *What I don't like*   Es dibujo – *It's art*

2. Gapped translation (sections 2–4)
a. *studying*   b. *lesson*   c. *best*   d. *can't stand*   e. *According*   f. *find*   g. *death*   h. *good*   i. *fun*

3. Translate into English (sections 2–4)
a. This subject   b. It's fascinating   c. According to me, it's useful   d. A good sense of humour
e. It's boring to death   f. It's fun   g. She is hard-working   h. I find it easy   i. I learn a lot

4. Broken words (section 4)
a. Asig**natura**   b. Ade**más**   c. Deb**eres**   d. Dif**í**cil   e. Útil   f. Bien   g. Mal

5. Missing vowels (section 4)
a. Divertido   b. Fácil   c. Difícil   d. Bien   e. Mal   f. Trabajador   g. Perezoso

6. Choose the correct translation
a. *I learn*   b. *boring*   c. *fun*   d. *IT*   e. *easy*   f. *hard*

7. Complete with the correct option from the box
a. lenguas   b. gusta   c. asignatura   d. parece   e. entiendo   f. mucho

8. Match the opposites
Aburrido – Divertido   Fácil – Difícil   Bueno – Malo   Bien – Mal   Menos – Más   Paciente – Impaciente
Trabajador – Perezoso

9. Gapped English to Spanish translation
a. que más   b. buen / humor   c. trabajadora / simpática   d. da / deberes   e. nunca / ayuda
f. explica / cosas   g. Aprendo / clases

10. Complete the table
I learn: **Aprendo**   *I understand:* **Entiendo**   *I find:* **Encuentro**   *He gives:* **Da**   *He/She doesn't get upset*: **No se enfada**   *He/She teaches:* **Enseña**   *He explains:* **Explica**   *I study:* **Estudio**   *What I like:* **Lo que me gusta**

11. Wordsearch

	M					E
	A	Ñ	E	S	N	E	S
O	L			O		S	P
R			S			T	A
T		D		M	N	U	Ñ
N	A	P	R	E	N	D	O
E			I	G		I	L
U		B		U		O	
C				S	N	G	N
N				T	I	Ü	I
E				A			P

I study: **Estudio**
He teaches: **Enseña**
He gives us: **Nos da**
I find: **Encuentro**
I learn: **Aprendo**
I like: **Me gusta**
Spanish: **Español**
Badly: **Mal**
Well: **Bien**

12. Guided translation
a. Explica bien   b. Lo encuentro difícil   c. No entiendo   d. Lo que más me gusta   e. Estudio ciencias
f. Nos da deberes   g. Se enfada fácilmente   h. Mi clase favorita   i. No aprendo nada
j. Me encanta la informática   k. Enseña muy mal

13. Translate into Spanish
a. En la escuela estudio matemáticas, química, dos lenguas extranjeras, dibujo, inglés, historia y gimnasia
b. Las asignaturas que me gustan más son el inglés y el español
c. Me encanta el español porque el profesor es divertido, las clases son divertidas y aprendo mucho
d. Lo que no soporto son las matemáticas porque las encuentro difíciles y el profesor explica las cosas mal
e. Mi profesor de inglés nos da demasiados deberes y se enfada fácilmente
f. En las clases de química no entiendo mucho. Sin embargo, en las clases de matemáticas aprendo mucho

THE LANGUAGE GYM

ANSWERS - UNIT 6 - Test (/100)

1. Vocabulary recognition – Spanish to English translation (/15)

a. IT	f. Easy	k. Hard-working
b. A subject	g. Because	l. He/she gets angry
c. I learn	h. Fun	m. Exciting
d. Art	i. Good	n. To study
e. Lazy	j. Bad	o. German

2. Syntax/Lexicogrammar – Split sentences (/5)

Yo pienso que esta	**asignatura es muy interesante**
La biologia	**es muy aburrida**
Estudio alemán y francés	**desde hace un año**
Lo encuentro	**emocionante y motivador**
Sin embargo, lo que	**no me gusta es la historia**

3. Grammar/Morphology/Vocabulary – Tangled translation (/20)

a. **Lo que** prefiero **estudiar**	g. Lo **encuentro** bastante **fácil**
b. **Es** muy **aburrido**	h. Me encanta el **español**
c. Es **inútil** en la **vida**	i. Tiene un buen **sentido** del humor
d. El profe **da** muchos **deberes**	j. Lo que yo no **soporto**, es la química
e. Es **demasiado** complicado	k. **Odio** esta **asignatura**
f. **A mi parecer**, es relajante	l. Mi **clase** favorita, es el **arte**

4. Translate into Spanish (/ 60 – each full sentence – 6 points)

a. Me gusta esta asignatura porque es emocionante y motivadora.

b. Finalmente, lo que odio es la química, porque es aburrida.

c. No soporto el arte, porque creo que es inútil en la vida.

d. Lo que más me gusta estudiar es la música.

e. No me gusta el alemán, porque es demasiado difícil.

f. No obstante, las matemáticas son realmente útiles.

g. Me gusta la geografía, pero no me gusta el teatro.

h. Lo que realmente odio es hacer/tomar un examen.

i. Me gusta bastante el español porque lo encuentro fácil y divertido.

j. Estudio/He estudiado música y arte desde hace cinco años.

 **THE LANGUAGE GYM**

Unit 7. My post 16 plans

KEY VOCABULARY Foundation

1. Mis opciones después del GCSE
Voy a: *I am going to*
-buscar un trabajo: *to look for a job*
-dejar el instituto: *leave school*
-dejar las matemáticas: *drop maths*
-elegir ciencias/idiomas para mis A Levels:
choose sciences/languages for my A Levels
-estudiar física/química/arte:
study physics/chemistry/art
-hacer el bachillerato: *take the baccalaureate*
-hacer A Levels: *take A Levels*
-hacer unas prácticas laborales:
do an apprenticeship
-seguir estudiando: *carry on studying*
-tomarme un año sabático: *take a gap year*
-trabajar de: *work as a...*
cocinero/a: *chef*
dependiente/a: *sales assistant*
peluquero/a: *hairdresser*

2. Adjetivos útiles
Porque es: *Because it's*
-creativo/a: *creative*
-difícil: *hard*
-emocionante: *exciting*
-enriquecedor/a: *enriching*
-fácil: *easy*
-fascinante: *fascinating*
-gratificante: *rewarding*
-útil: *useful*

3. Expresiones esenciales
En la universidad: *At university*
El año que viene: *Next year*
Es importante para el futuro:
It's important for the future
Esto me apasiona: *I am passionate about this*
Me gustaría: *I would like*
Pienso que: *I think that*
Prefiero tomarme mi tiempo:
I prefer to take my time
Se me <u>da</u> bien esta asignatura:
I am good at this subject
Se me <u>dan</u> bien las ciencias:
I am good at science
Si fuera posible: *If it were possible*
Si pudiera: *If I could*
Ya que me interesa: *As it interests me*

1. Match (section 1)

Hacer A Levels	*An apprenticeship*
Prácticas laborales	*To do A Levels*
Elegir idiomas	*To look for a job*
Dejar el instituto	*To carry on studying*
Buscar un trabajo	*Sales assistant*
Estudiar química	*To study chemistry*
Dejar de estudiar el arte	*To leave school*
Trabajar de	*To choose languages*
Seguir estudiando	*To drop art*
Dependiente	*To work as a*

2. Gapped translation (section 1)

a. Dejar el instituto: *To _____ school*

b. Hacer prácticas laborales: *To do an _____*

c. Trabajar como médico: *To work as a _____*

d. Estudiar química: *To _____ chemistry*

e. Ir a la universidad: *To go to _____*

f. Elegir idiomas para los A Levels: *Choose _____ for my A levels*

g. Buscar un trabajo: *To look for a _____*

3. Choose the correct translation (sections 1–2)

a. Dejar: *to drop / to choose / to look for*

b. Emocionante: *easy / fun / exciting*

c. Elegir: *to leave / to drop / to choose*

d. Útil: *useful / easy / challenging*

e. Gratificante: *free / rewarding / interesting*

f. Creativo: *creator / creating / creative*

g. Dependiente: *chef / sales assistant / apprentice*

h. Buscar: *to drop / to look for / to learn*

4. Faulty translation (sections 2–3)

a. Se me da bien: *I am bad at this*

b. Esto me apasiona: *I am emotional about this*

c. Ya que me interesa un poco: *As it interests me a lot*

d. Si fuera posible: *If it were impossible*

e. Es difícil: *It's easy*

f. Para el futuro: *Stop the future*

g. Luego: *Before*

5. Wordsearch – Find the Spanish for the listed words

E	S	T	U	D	I	A	R	E
S	L	I	C	Í	F	I	D	R
T	I	E	W	A	N	B	H	I
S	T	M	R	C	E	U	R	N
H	Ú	P	A	D	R	S	U	A
F	I	O	L	A	N	C	V	M
D	K	T	R	A	B	A	J	O
A	E	L	E	G	I	R	A	R
R	T	J	G	A	F	E	Y	U
Y	L	N	A	Ü	I	A	L	T
M	I	R	A	R	N	M	I	U
P	I	E	N	S	O	R	L	F

To look for:

Job:

Future:

Difficult:

Useful:

Choose:

Time:

I think:

To study:

To drop (leave):

6. Complete the table

English	Español
Work	
Hard	
	Año
	Pienso que
	Estudiar
	Buscar
To work as	
To drop	

7. Gapped English to Spanish translation

a. ___ fuera posible: *If it were possible*

b. _____ un trabajo: *To look for a job*

c. Voy _____ estudiar: *I am going to study*

d. Ya que es _____: *Seeing as it's useful*

e. _____: *To take*

f. Un _____ sabático: *A sabbatical year*

g. Dejar el_____: *To quit school*

h. ____ que es duro: *As it's hard*

i. _____ ciencias: *To choose science*

j. Voy a _____ : *I am going to do*

k. Seguir _____ : *To carry on studying*

l. _____ de estudiar el teatro: *To drop drama*

m. Buscar un _____ : *To look for a job*

n. _____ que: *I think that*

o. _____ como chef: *To work as a chef*

p. Tomarme mi _____ : *To take my time*

q. Si _____ : *If I could*

r. _____ el bachillerato: *To take my baccalaureate*

8. Add in the missing words

a. Voy a b_ _ _ _ _ un trab_ _ _

b. Voy a h_ _ _ _ mi bachillerato

c. Voy a t_ _ _ _ _ _ _ como abogado

d. S_ f_ _ _ _ pos_ _ _ _, me gustaría estud_ _ _ español

e. Me gustaría tomar un a_ _ s_ _ _ _ _ _ _

f. Voy a d_ _ _ _ el instituto

i. V_ _ a trabajar c_ _ _ dependiente

j. Voy a e_ _ _ _ _ _ _ lenguas y_ que s_ _ útiles

9. Translate into Spanish

a. I am going to go

b. I am going to look for

c. I am going to continue

d. I am going to choose

e. I am going to drop

f. I am going to do

g. I am going to work

h. I am going to take

10. English to Spanish translation

a. If it were possible, I would like to carry on studying

b. I am going to take a gap year

c. I would like to do an apprenticeship

d. I am going to work as a chef in a restaurant

e. I am going to study maths because I am good at it

f. If it were possible, I would like to go to university in Spain

KEY VOCABULARY Higher

1. Lo que haré después del colegio

El año próximo: *Next year*
Cuando haya terminado el instituto:
When I have finished secondary school
Me gustaría mucho: *I would like a lot*
Ojalá pueda: *I hope I can*
-hacer A Levels: *take A Levels*
-hacer el bachillerato: *take the baccalaureate*
Me gustaría tomar un año sabático:
I will take a gap year...
-en el extranjero: *abroad*
-en Australia: *in Australia*
Haré unas prácticas laborales para hacerme:
I will do an apprenticeship to become a:
-albañil: *builder*
-dependiente/a: *sales assistant*
-fontanero/a: *plumber*
-peluquero/a: *hairdresser*
Voy a buscar trabajo en:
I am going to look for a job in
-el cáterin: *catering*
-la industria hotelera: *hospitality*
-ventas: *sales*

2. Si sigo estudiando…

Creo/pienso que: *I believe/think that*
Voy a elegir humanidades para mis A Levels:
I am going to choose humanities for my A Levels
Voy a estudiar: *I am going to study*
Voy a dejar de estudiar: *I am going to drop*
-arte: *art*
-teatro: *drama*

3. Lo que voy a hacer en la universidad

Después, en la universidad:
Afterwards, at university
Para mis estudios superiores:
For my further studies
Tengo la intención de: *I intend*
Estoy contemplando: *I am contemplating*
-una carrera de ciencias: *a scientific career*
-hacer un máster de empresariales:
a Masters in Business
Todavía no sé lo que quiero hacer:
I don't know yet what I want to do
Probablemente voy a estudiar:
I am probably going to study
-idiomas: *languages*
-medicina *medicine*
No tengo ni idea de lo que voy a estudiar:
I have no idea what I am going to study

1. Match

Buscar	*To look for*
Ojalá pueda	*Carry on studying*
Albañil	*To drop*
Estudiar	*Builder*
Química	*Take A Levels*
Seguir estudiando	*Salesperson*
Dependiente	*I hope I can*
Elegir	*To choose*
Hacer A Levels	*Foreign*
Extranjeras	*Chemistry*
Dejar	*To study*

2. Gapped translation

a. Voy a hacer: *I am going to _____*

b. Buscar un trabajo: *To _____ a job*

c. Voy a estudiar: *I am going to _____*

d. Un trabajo en ventas: *A job in _____*

e. Cuando haya terminado: *When I _____*

f. Para mis estudios superiores: *For my _____*

g. No tengo ni idea: *I have _____*

h. Todavía no sé: *I don't _____ yet*

i. Estudiar empresariales: *To _____ business*

j. Quiero hacer: *I _____ do*

3. Translate into English

a. Voy a dejar de estudiar química

b. Voy a buscar un trabajo como dependiente

c. Voy a tomar un año sabático en el extranjero

d. Voy a estudiar lenguas extranjeras

e. Voy a hacer unas prácticas laborales

f. No tengo ni idea de lo que voy a estudiar

4. Broken words

a. As_____ : *Subject*
b. Estu_____ : *To study*
c. Ven_____ : *Sales*
d. Bus____ : *To look for*
e. Trab_____ : *Job*
f. Len____ : *Languages*
g. Rea_____ : *Really*
h. Tod_____ : *Yet*

5. Missing vowels

a. P _ _ ns _ q _ _
b. M _ s _ st _ d _ _ s
c. D _ p _ nd _ _ nt _
d. B _ sc _ r
e. _ l _ ñ _ pr _ x _ m _
f. Tr _ b _ j _
g. Pr _ ct _ c _ s l _ b _ r _ l _ s

6. Choose the correct translation

a. Buscar: *to learn / to study / to look for*

b. Todavía: *already / later / yet, still*

c. Derecho: *law / English /art*

d. Asignaturas: *subjects / sectors / choices*

e. Ventas *job / hospitality / sales*

f. Arte: *biology / chemistry / art*

7. Complete with the correct option from the box

a. Voy a estudiar _____ extranjeras

b. Voy a _____ estudiando

c. No tengo _____ idea

d. Quiero _____ medicina

e. Para mis _____ superiores

f. Voy a _____ abogado

| estudiar |
| lenguas |
| estudios |
| ni |
| ser |
| seguir |

8. Anagrams

a. saVent

b. naMecidi

c. Estuddoian

d. baraTjo

e. Barcus

f. cráPticas baloesral

9. Sentence puzzle

a. de hacer Tengo la carrera de derecho la intención

b. el bachillerato gustaría Me hacer

c. Voy un industria trabajo a buscar en la hotelera

d. fontanero laborales Me gustaría hacer de prácticas

e. No voy a estudiar ni idea de lo que tengo

f. Voy de estudiar y el a dejar el inglés dibujo

g. sabático en un año tomar Voy a Australia

10. Complete the table

English	Español
I am going to look for	
	Un trabajo
I am going to study	
I have no idea	
	Lo que quiero
	Dejar
Foreign languages	
	Voy a elegir
My studies	

11. Guided translation

a. *I have no idea*: N_ t_____ n___ i_____

b. *I am going to choose*: V_____ a e_____

c. *What I want to study*: L_ q__ q_____ e_____

d. *To study medicine*: E_____ m_____

e. *Scientific subjects*: L__ a_____ c_____

f. *I am going to study*: V____ a e_____

g. *I intend*: T_____ l_ i_____ d__

h. *I am going to drop*: V___ a d_____

i. *I am going to look for a job in sales*: V_____ a b_____ u__ t_____ e__ v_____

j. *I am going to take a gap year*: V_____ a t_____ u___ a_____ s_____

12. Translate into Spanish

a. Next year, I would like to go to university in Madrid

b. I am going to drop chemistry and maths because it's too difficult

c. I have no idea what I want to study after my GCSE exams

d. After my baccalaureate exams, I would like to go to university to do a degree in medicine

e. I don't know what to study yet, but I think I will continue to study foreign languages

f. I am going to do an apprenticeship to become a builder or a plumber

g. If I carry on studying at school, I am probably going to study science and maybe drama

UNIT 7 - Test (/100)

1. Vocabulary recognition: Spanish to English translation (/15)

a. Un trabajo	f. Elegir	k. Dependiente
b. Dejar	g. Voy a estudiar	l. Buscar
c. Seguir estudiando	h. Útil	m. Emocionante
d. Estudiar medicina	i. Pienso que	n. Se me da bien
e. La escuela	j. Si pudiera	o. Luego

2. Syntax/Lexicogrammar – Split sentences (/5)

Se me da bien	**dependiente**
Voy a ir	**fascinante**
Me encanta porque es	**al instituto**
Me gustaría trabajar como	**año sabático**
Voy a tomar un	**esta asignatura**

3. Grammar/Morphology/Vocabulary – Tangled translation (/20)

a. Voy a **to do** el **baccalaureate**   g. **I will do** unas **apprenticeship**

b. Voy a **drop** el **art**   h. **Because** es **hard**

c. Voy a **look for** un **job**   i. **This** no me **interests**

d. Voy a continuar mis **studies**   j. Voy a **carry on studying**

e. Pienso **that** voy a trabajar **as** cocinero   k. Es importante **for** el **future**

f. Esta **is not** una asignatura **useful**   l. Se me da bien esta **subject**

4. Translate into Spanish (/ 60 – each full sentence – 6 points)

a. Next year, if I could, I would like to carry on studying.

b. Afterwards, I would like to study maths at university.

c. I will study chemistry because I am good at this subject.

d. I want to study languages because I am passionate about it.

e. I think that after my exams, I will take a sabbatical year.

f. For my further studies, I intend to do a law degree.

g. I will do an apprenticeship to become a builder or a plumber.

h. For the moment, I am going to look for a job in catering.

i. It's an important decision, therefore I prefer to take my time.

j. I would like to work as a lawyer because it is well paid.

THE LANGUAGE GYM

ANSWERS - Unit 7. My post 16 plans - Foundation

1. Match (section 1)
Hacer A Levels – *To do A Levels*   Prácticas laborales – *To do an apprenticeship*
Elegir idiomas – *To choose languages*   Dejar el instituto – *To leave school*
Buscar un trabajo – *To look for a job*   Estudiar química – *To study chemistry*
Dejar de estudiar el arte – *To drop art*   Trabajar de – *To work as a*
Seguir estudiando – *To continue my studies*   Dependiente – *Sales assistant*

2. Gapped translation (section 1)
a. leave b. apprenticeship c. doctor d. study e. university f. languages g. job

3. Choose the correct translation (sections 1–2)
a. to drop b. exciting c. to choose d. useful e. rewarding f. creative g. sales assistant h. to look for

4. Faulty translation (sections 2–3)
a. Se me da bien: *I am **good** at this* b. Esto me apasiona: *I am **passionate** about this*
c. Ya que me interesa un poco: *As it interests me **a bit*** d. Si fuera posible: *If it were **possible***
e. Es difícil: *It's **hard/difficult*** f. Para el futuro: ***For the future*** g. Luego: ***Afterwards***

5. Wordsearch

E	S	T	U	D	I	A	R	
	L	I	C	Í	F	I	D	
	I	E				B		
	T	M				U		
	Ú	P				S		
		O				C		
D		T	R	A	B	A	J	O
	E	L	I	G	I	R		R
	J							U
		A						T
			R					U
P	I	E	N	S	O			F

To look for:	**Buscar**
Job:	**Trabajo**
Future:	**Futuro**
Difficult:	**Difícil**
Useful:	**Útil**
Choose:	**Elegir**
Time:	**Tiempo**
I think:	**Pienso**
To study:	**Estudiar**
To drop (leave):	**Dejar**

6. Complete the table
Work: **Trabajo** *Hard:* **Difícil/Duro** *Year:* **Año** *I think that:* **Pienso que** *To study:* **Estudiar**
To look for: **Buscar** *To work as:* **Trabajar de/como** *To drop:* **Dejar**

7. Gapped English to Spanish translation
a. **Si** fuera posible b. **Buscar** un trabajo c. Voy **a** estudiar d. Ya que es **útil** e. **Tomar** f. Un **año** sabático
g. Dejar el **colegio** h. **Ya** que es **duro** i. **Elegir** ciencias j. Voy a **hacer** k. Seguir **estudiando**
l. **Dejar** de estudiar teatro m. Buscar un **trabajo** n. **Pienso** que o. **Trabajar** como chef
p. Tomarme mi **tiempo** q. Si **pudiera** r. **Tomar/Hacer** mi bachillerato

8. Add in the missing words
a. buscar / trabajo b. hacer c. trabajar d. Si fuera posible / estudiar e. año sabático f. dejar
i. Voy / como j. estudiar / ya / son

9. Translate into Spanish
a. Voy a ir b. Voy a buscar c. Voy a seguir/continuar d. Voy a elegir e. Voy a dejar (de)
f. Voy a hacer g. Voy a trabajar h. Voy a tomar

10. English to Spanish translation
a. Si fuera posible, me gustaría seguir estudiando
b. Voy a tomar un año sabático
c. Me gustaría hacer unas prácticas laborales
d. Voy a trabajar como chef/cocinero en un restaurante
e. Voy a estudiar matemáticas porque se me dan bien
f. Si fuera posible, me gustaría ir a la universidad en España

ANSWERS - Unit 7. My post 16 plans - Higher

1. Match

Buscar – *To look for*   Ojalá pueda – *I hope I can*   Albañil – *Builder*   Estudiar – *To study*
Química – *Chemistry*   Seguir estudiando – *Carry on studying*   Dependiente – *Sales assistant*
Elegir – *To choose* Hacer A Levels – *Take A Levels*   Extranjeras – *Foreign*   Dejar – *To drop*

2. Gapped translation

a. *do* b. *look for* c. *study* d. *sales* e. *finish* f. *further studies* g. *no idea* h. *know* i. *study* j. *want*

3. Translate into English

a. I am going to drop chemistry   b. I am going to look for a job as a sales assistant
c. I am going to take a gap year abroad   d. I am going to study foreign languages
e. I am going to do an apprenticeship   f. I have no idea what I am going to study

4. Broken words

a. As**ignatura**   b. Estu**diar**   c. Ven**tas**   d. Bus**car**   e. Trab**ajo**   f. Len**guas**   g. Rea**lmente**   h. Tod**avía**

5. Missing vowels

a. Pienso que   b. Mis estudios   c. Dependiente   d. Buscar   e. El año próximo   f. Trabajo   g. Prácticas laborales

6. Choose the correct translation

a. to look for   b. yet   c. law   d. subjects   e. sales   f. art

7. Complete with the correct option from the box

a. **lenguas**   b. **seguir**   c. **ni**   d. **estudiar**   e. **estudios**   f. **ser**

8. Anagrams

a. Ventas   b. Medicina   c. Estudiando   d. Trabajo   e. Buscar   f. Prácticas laborales

9. Sentence puzzle

a. Tengo la intención de hacer la carrera de derecho   b. Me gustaría hacer el bachillerato
c. Voy a buscar un trabajo en la industria hotelera   d. Me gustaría hacer prácticas laborales de fontanero
e. No tengo ni idea de lo que voy a estudiar   f. Voy a dejar de estudiar el inglés y el dibujo
g. Voy a tomar un año sabático en Australia

10. Complete the table

I am going to look for: **Voy a buscar**   *A job:* **Un trabajo**   *I am going to study:* **Voy a estudiar**
I have no idea: **No tengo ni idea**   *What I want:* **Lo que quiero**   *To drop:* **Dejar**
Foreign languages: **Lenguas extranjeras**   *I am going to choose:* **Voy a elegir**   *My studies:* **Mis estudios**

11. Guided translation

a. No tengo ni idea   b. Voy a elegir   c. Lo que quiero estudiar   d. Estudiar medicina
e. Las asignaturas científicas   f. Voy a estudiar   g. Tengo la intención de   h. Voy a dejar
i. Voy a buscar un trabajo en ventas   j. Voy a tomar un año sabático

12. Translate into Spanish

a. El año que viene me gustaría ir a la universidad en Madrid.
b. Voy a dejar (de estudiar) química y matemáticas porque son demasiado difíciles.
c. No tengo ni idea de lo que quiero estudiar después de mis exámenes GCSE.
d. Después de mis exámenes de bachillerato, me gustaría ir a la universidad para hacer la carrera de medicina.
e. Todavía no sé qué estudiar, pero creo que voy a seguir estudiando lenguas extranjeras.
f. Voy a hacer unas prácticas laborales para hacerme albañil o fontanero.
g. Si sigo estudiando en el colegio, probablemente voy a estudiar ciencias y tal vez drama.

 THE LANGUAGE GYM

ANSWERS - UNIT 7 - Test (/100)

1. Vocabulary recognition: Spanish to English translation (/15)

a. A job

b. To drop

c. To carry on studying

d. To study medicine

e. School

f. To choose

g. I am going to study

h. Useful

i. I think that

j. If I could

k. Sales assistant

l. To look for

m. Exciting

n. I am good at it

o. Afterwards/Then

2. Syntax/Lexicogrammar – Split sentences (/5)

Se me da bien	**esta asignatura**
Voy a ir	**al instituto**
Me encanta porque es	**fascinante**
Me gustaría trabajar como	**dependiente**
Voy a tomar un	**año sabático**

3. Grammar/Morphology/Vocabulary – Tangled translation (/20)

a. Voy a **hacer** el **bachillerato**

b. Voy a **dejar** el **arte**

c. Voy a **buscar** un **trabajo**

d. Voy a continuar mis **estudios**

e. Pienso **que** voy a trabajar **como** cocinero

f. Esta **no es** una asignatura **útil**

g. **Haré** unas **prácticas laborales**

h. **Porque** es **duro/difícil**

i. **Esto** no me **interesa**

j. Voy a **seguir estudiando**

k. Es importante **para** el **futuro**

l. Se me da bien esta **asignatura**

4. Translate into Spanish (/ 60 – each full sentence – 6 points)

a. El año que viene, si pudiera, me gustaría seguir estudiando.

b. Después/Luego, me gustaría estudiar matemáticas en la universidad.

c. Estudiaré química porque se me da bien esta asignatura.

d. Quiero estudiar idiomas porque me apasionan.

e. Creo que después de mis exámenes, tomaré un año sabático.

f. Para mis estudios superiores, tengo la intención de hacer una carrera de derecho.

g. Voy a hacer unas prácticas laborales para ser albañil o fontanero.

g. De momento, voy a buscar trabajo en hostelería.

i. Es una decisión importante, así que prefiero tomarme mi tiempo.

j. Me gustaría trabajar como abogado porque está bien pagado.

THE LANGUAGE GYM

Unit 8. What job I would like to do and why

KEY VOCABULARY Foundation

1. Los trabajos (jobs)

Cuando termine mis estudios:
When I finish my studies

Me gustaría trabajar como:
I would like to work as a/an

Me gustaría ser:
I would like to become a/an

- abogado/a: *lawyer*
- artesano/a: *artisan*
- cirujano/a: *surgeon*
- dependiente/a: *shop assistant*
- electricista: *electrician*
- enfermero/a: *nurse*
- fontanero: *plumber*
- hombre de negocios: *businessman*
- informático/a: *IT worker*
- ingeniero/a: *engineer*
- médico/a: *doctor*
- mujer de negocios: *businesswoman*
- músico/a: *musician*
- peluquero/a: *hairdresser*
- profesor/a: *teacher*
- veterinario/a: *vet*

2. El tipo de trabajo que quiero

Me gustaría un trabajo:
I would like a/an ... job

- al aire libre: *outdoors*
- de oficina: *office*
- en informática: *IT*
- en ventas: *sales*

Hacer trabajo voluntario:
To do volunteer work

3. Por qué me interesa

Porque es: *Because it is*
- agradable: *pleasant*
- gratificante: *rewarding*
- importante: *important*
- útil: *useful*
- variado: *varied*

Y porque te permite: *And it allows you to*
- ayudar a los demás: *help others*
- estar en contacto con la naturaleza:
be in touch with nature
- ganar mucho dinero:
earn a lot of money
- viajar: *travel*

1. Complete the table (section 1)

English	Español (masculine)	Español (feminine)
electrician	electricista	
	enfermero	
lawyer	abogado	
		peluquera
surgeon		
	dependiente	
	cocinero	
		informática
musician		

2. Broken words (section 1)

a. Arte_ _ _ _ : *Artisan (F)*

b. Fonta_ _ _ _ : *Plumber (M)*

c. Inge_ _ _ _ _ : *Engineer (M)*

d. Tra_ _ _ _: *Job*

e. Mús_ _ _ : *Musician (F)*

f. Trab_ _ _ _ : *To work*

g. Abo_ _ _ _ : *Lawyer (F)*

h. Estu_ _ _ _ : *Studies*

3. Translate into English (section 1)

a. Profesor:

b. Dependiente:

c. Hacerse:

d. Seré:

e. Artesano:

f. Cirujana:

g. Cocinero:

4. Faulty translation (sections 1–2) – Correct the wrong English translations

a. Me gustaría un buen trabajo: *I would like a good salary*

b. Un trabajo de oficina: *An outdoor job*

c. Un trabajo voluntario: *A job in the army*

d. Me gustaría trabajar: *I would like to travel*

e. Seré peluquero: *I will be a builder*

f. Me gustaría ser: *I would like to travel*

g. Un trabajo al aire libre: *An outdoor job*

h. Un trabajo en informática: *An IT job*

5. Circle the 6 positive adjectives on the list and translate them into English (section 2)

a. Agradable	e. Bien pagado	i. Gratificante
b. Mal pagado	f. Útil	j. Asqueroso
c. Agotador	g. Importante	k. Sucio
d. Duro	h. Fascinante	l. Malo

6. Complete the English translation

a. Me gustaría hacer trabajo voluntario: *I would like to do* _____ *work*

b. Cuando termine mis estudios... *When I* _____ *my studies...*

c. ...me gustaría ser cirujano: *...I would like to become a* _____

d. Me gustaría ser piloto porque es variado: *I would like to be a* _____, *because it is*_____

e. Me gustaría un trabajo al aire libre: *I would like an* _____ _____

f. Voy a hacerme hombre de negocios: *I am going to become a* _____ *man*

g. Me gustaría ser médica, como mi madre: *I would like to become a* _____, *like my mother*

h. Quiero estar en contacto con la naturaleza: *I want to be in touch with* _____

---

7. Wordsearch – Find the Spanish for the listed words

M	A	Y	U	D	A	R	E	R	T
A	L	C	P	S	E	N	D	T	O
R	A	S	I	A	N	A	I	U	A
A	I	O	S	D	T	R	N	R	R
V	R	I	P	O	É	B	E	G	O
I	E	C	R	N	T	M	R	I	S
L	L	O	E	U	R	A	O	A	E
L	I	G	G	E	M	I	T	G	F
O	B	E	F	L	O	N	Ü	N	O
S	R	N	T	O	E	A	D	I	R
O	E	X	I	V	N	L	A	V	P
A	Z	E	L	A	R	U	T	A	N

Nurse: E

Doctor: M

Teacher: P

Outdoor: A

Nature: N

Business: N

To help: A

Money: D

Sales: V

---

8. Complete (section 3)

a. Ganar mucho d_ _ _ _ _

b. Un trabajo b_ _ _ pagado

c. Voy a _ _ _ profesor

d. Porque _ _ variado

e. Un trabajo vol_ _ _ _ _ _ _

f. Es muy gratif_ _ _ _ _ _

g. Te p_ _ _ _ _ _ viajar

h. Ayudar a los d_ _ _ _

i. Un trabajo en ve_ _ _ _

j. Un trabajo al aire l_ _ _ _

---

9. Translate into Spanish

a. Job:

b. Lawyer (F):

c. Money:

d. Varied

e. Well paid:

f. Sales assistant (M):

g. Pleasant:

h. I would like to be:

---

10. Guided translation

a. *When I finish my studies*: C_____ t_____ m__ e_____

b. *A job in sales*: U__ t_____ e__ v_____

c. *I would like to become*: M__ g_____ s_____

d. *An outdoor job*: U__ t_____ a__ a____ l_____

e. *I will become a teacher*: V__ a s_____ p_____

f. *I would like to work as*: M__ g_____ t_____ c_____

g. *An office job*: U___ t_____ d__ o_____

h. *To do volunteer work*: H_____ t_____ v_____

---

11. English to Spanish translation

a. I would like to work as a pilot because this allows me to travel.

b. I would like to work as a teacher because it is rewarding.

c. I would like to become a surgeon because it is a well-paid job.

d. I would like to become a lawyer because it is fun.

e. I would like an outdoor job because I would like to in touch with nature.

f. I would like to work as a taxi driver because it's varied.

THE LANGUAGE GYM

KEY VOCABULARY Higher
1. Lo que quiero hacer después de mis estudios
Cuando termine mis estudios: *After my studies*
Una vez que tenga mi título:
Once I have my diploma...
Me gustaría trabajar como: *I would like to work as*
Me gustaría ser: *I would like to be*
-cirujano/a: *surgeon* -contable: *accountant*
-dependiente/a: *shop assistant*
-informático/a: *IT worker*
-profesor/a: *teacher*
2. Por qué me interesa esta profesión
Es la carrera de mis sueños:
I dream of doing this career
(No) Quiero hacer este trabajo porque me parece:
I (don't) want to do this work because it seems
-agotador/a: *tiring*
-estresante: *stressful*
-exigente: *demanding*
-gratificante: *rewarding*
-lucrativo: *lucrative*
En mi opinión / A mi parecer:
In my opinion / According to me
Es una actividad que es bastante lucrativa:
It's an activity which is quite lucrative
Es un sector que está en auge:
It's a sector which is fast-growing
Es una industria que está de moda:
It's an industry which is fashionable
Esta profesión me permitirá:
This profession will allow me
-ayudar a los demás: *to help others*
-trabajar en equipo: *to work as a team*
-viajar: *to travel*
3. Los consejos (*advice*) de mis parientes y amigos
Según mis amigos: *According to my friends*
Mis padres me dicen que: *My parents tell me that*
Mi hermano me dice que: *My brother tells me that*
Mis profesores piensan que: *My teachers think that*
-debería hacer carrera en ventas:
I should do a career in sales
-debería estudiar medicina en la universidad:
I should do medecine at university
-debería trabajar como: *I should work as a/an*
-arquitecto/a: *architect*
-entrenador/a deportivo/a: *sport instructor*
-periodista: *journalist*
4. Mi opinión (*My opinion*)
Yo prefiero: *I prefer*
-el trabajo independiente: *independent work*
-los trabajos al aire libre: *outdoor jobs*
-los trabajos de oficina: *office jobs*
-los trabajos manuales: *manual work*

1. Match

Ventas	*Others*
Agotador	*Fast-growing*
En auge	*Once*
Artesano/a	*Sales*
Viajar	*Tiring*
Los demás	*Salesperson*
Vendedor/a	*To travel*
Una vez	*As*
Como	*Craftsperson*

2. Gapped translation
a. Después de mis estudios: *After my* _____
b. A mi parecer: *In my* _____
c. Según mis amigos: _____ *my friends*
d. Mis padres me dicen: *My parents* _____ *me*
e. Debería hacer: *I* _____ *do*
f. Quiero ser: *I want to* _____
g. Está de moda: *It's very* _____

3. Broken words
a. Los d _ _ _ _ : *The others*
b. Equi_ _ : *Team*
c. Esta car_ _ _ _ : *This career*
d. Una indus_ _ _ _ : *An industry*
e. Ele_ _ _ : *To choose*
f. Ven_ _ _ : *Sales*

4. Faulty translation – Correct the wrong English translations. NOTE: Not all are wrong!
a. Los trabajos de oficina: *Outdoor jobs*
b. A mi parecer: *According to me*
c. Los trabajos al aire libre: *Manual work*
d. Debería trabajar: *I should go*
e. Mi amigo me dice que: *My friend thinks that*
f. Mis profes piensan que: *My teachers say that*
g. Un sector en auge: *A slow-growing sector*

 **THE LANGUAGE GYM**

5. Translate into English (all sections)

a. Un trabajo independiente

b. Un trabajo de oficina

c. A mi parecer

d. En auge

e. Agotador

f. Al aire libre

g. Mis amigos me dicen que

h. Debería hacer medicina

i. Mis profesores piensan que

j. Me parece exigente

k. Trabajar en equipo

l. Una carrera en ventas

6. Missing vowels: jobs

a. _b_g_d_

b. _rt_s_n_

c. c_nt_bl_

d. pr_f_s_r

e. _nf_rm_t_c_

f. _rq__t_ct_

7. Complete with the missing words

a. Un _____ independiente

b. En a_____

c. Es _____ exigente

d. Me _____ hacerme artesano

e. Una carrera _____ ventas

f. Cuando _____ mis estudios

8. Sentence puzzle

a. es un La informática fascinante y está que sector en auge

b. A mi debería ser, creo que parecer abogado

c. de me gustaría mis estudios, trabajar como Después contable

d. Mis dicen amigos tener una carrera que debería en ventas

e. prefiero los Yo de trabajos oficina

f. Mi mayor me hermano debería trabajar dice que como periodista

9. Complete the table

English	Español
	En auge
I would like to be	
	Los trabajos de oficina
According to me	
	Entrenador deportivo
	Mis amigos dicen
Demanding	
	Hacer una carrera
A manual job	

10. Wordsearch – Find the Spanish for the listed words

N	T	R	A	B	A	J	O	I
S	U	E	V	I	Ü	G	N	P
E	M	N	M	N	O	D	T	A
C	G	E	F	P	U	E	R	V
T	R	O	R	S	L	O	P	E
O	E	M	T	E	D	E	M	N
R	P	R	P	A	T	I	O	T
E	I	E	T	N	A	R	G	A
A	L	O	S	D	E	M	Á	S
B	G	D	R	I	F	S	O	P
A	O	N	A	S	E	T	rt	A

Tiring: A

Employment: E

Others: L

Sales: V

Sector: S

Craftsman: A

Job: T

Industry: I

11. Guided translation

a. Fast-growing sector: U_ s _____ e__ a_____

b. According to me: A m__ p_____

c. I would like to become: M_ g_____ s____

d. An office job: U_ t_____ d_ o_____

e. I would like to work: M_ g_____ t_____

f. After my studies: D_____ d__ m__ e_____

g. To work in sales: T_____ e__ v_____

h. It will allow me: M_ p_____

i. Sports instructor: E_____ d_____

12. Translate into Spanish

a. After my studies, I would like to work as a surgeon.

b. I like this job, as it will allow me to travel.

c. This job seems demanding, but not stressful.

d. I should do a career in sales.

e. My parents say that I should study medicine.

f. My brother tells me I should work as a teacher.

g. I prefer outdoor jobs, so I would like to be a farmer.

h. This job will allow me to help others.

i. I dream of having this career, as I think this profession is fascinating.

UNIT 8 - Test (/100)

1. Vocabulary recognition - Spanish to English translation (/15)

a. Mis estudios

b. Título

c. Fontanero

d. Me gustaría

e. Un trabajo

f. Agotador

g. Voy a ser

h. Artesano

i. Oficina

j. Al aire libre

k. Ayudar

l. Dependiente

m. Emocionante

n. Te permite

o. Ganar

2. Syntax/Lexicogrammar – Split sentences (/5)

Este trabajo te permite	**mucho dinero**
Quiero trabajar	**viajar**
Mi trabajo me permitirá estar en	**como mi padre**
Me gustaría ganar	**al aire libre**
Voy a ser profesor,	**contacto con la naturaleza**

3. Grammar/Morphology/Vocabulary – Tangled translation (/20)

a. Voy a ser **plumber**

b. **I would like** un trabajo **well paid**

c. **According to** mis **friends**

d. **I want** hacer **this job**

e. Me gustaría tener un trabajo **outdoors**

f. Me gustaría **become an engineer**

g. **I prefer** el trabajo **independent**

h. Es una **industry which** es lucrativa

i. Me gustaría **work** como **craftsman**

j. Mis padre me **tell that** debería ser médico

k. Está **in fashion** en **this** momento

l. Me gustaría hacer una **career** en **sales**

4. Translate into Spanish (/ 60 – each full sentence – 6 points)

a. Once I have my diploma, I would like to become an accountant.

b. I like this profession because it will allow me to travel.

c. My parents say that I should study medicine at university.

d. I prefer independent work, so I would like to be a lawyer.

e. My friends say I should try to work as a sports instructor.

f. For me, I prefer outdoor jobs, so I could be a farmer.

g. In my opinion, it's a sector which is fast-growing at the moment.

h. According to me this is an industry which is quite lucrative nowadays.

i. My brother says I should try to do a career in sales.

j. I dream of having this career as I think this profession is very rewarding.

 **THE LANGUAGE GYM**

61

Unit 8. What job I would like to do and why - Foundation

1. Complete the table (section 1)
Electrician: **Electricista**   *Nurse*: **Enfermero/a**   *Lawyer*: **Abogado/a**   *Hairdresser*: **Peluquero/a**
Surgeon: **Cirujano/a**   *Shop assistant*: **Dependiente/a**   *Chef*: **Cocinero/a**   *IT worker*: **Informático/a**
Musician: **Músico/a**

2. Broken words (section 1)
a. Arte**sana**   b. Fonta**nero**   c. Inge**niero**   d. Tra**bajo**   e. Mús**ica**   f.Tra**bajar**   g. Abo**gada**   h. Estu**dios**

3. Translate into English (section 1)
a. Teacher   b. Sales assistant   c. To become   d. I will be   e. Craftsman   f. Surgeon   g. Chef

4. Faulty translation (sections 1–2) – Correct the wrong English translations
a. Me gustaría un buen trabajo: *I would like a good **job***   b. Trabajo de oficina: *An **office** job*
c. Un trabajo voluntario: *A job in the **volunteering sector***   d. Me gustaría trabajar: *I would like to **work***
e. Seré peluquero: *I will be a **hairdresser***   f. Me gustaría ser: *I would like to **be/become***
g. Un trabajo al aire libre: *An outdoor job* √   h. Un trabajo en informática: *An IT job* √

5. Circle the 6 positive adjectives on the list and translate them into English (section 2)
a. Agradable: *Pleasant*   b -   c -   d -   e. Bien pagado: *Well-paid*   f. Útil: *Useful*   g. Importante: *Important*
h. Fascinante: *Fascinating*   i. Gratificante: *Rewarding*   j. -   k. -   l. -

6. Complete the English translation
a. volunteer/volunteering   b. finish   c. surgeon   d. pilot / varied   e. outdoor job   f. business
g. doctor   h. nature

7. Wordsearch

	A	Y	U	D	A	R			
	L	C				D			
	A	S	I			I			A
	I	O		D			N	R	R
	R	I		É		E			O
	E	C			M	R			S
	L	O		R		O	A		E
	I	G		E			T		F
	B	E	F		N				O
	R	N		E					R
	E		V						P
A	Z	E	L	A	R	U	T	A	N

Nurse: **Enfermera**
Doctor: **Médica**
Teacher: **Profesora**
Outdoor: **Al aire libre**
Nature: **Naturaleza**
Business: **Negocios**
To help: **Ayudar**
Money: **Dinero**
Sales: **Ventas**

8. Complete (section 3)
a. **di**nero   b. **bien** c. **ser**   d. **es**   e. vol**untario**   f. gratif**icante**   g. **permite**   h. de**más**   i. ve**ntas**   j. **libre**

9. Translate into Spanish
a. Trabajo   b. Abogada   c. Dinero   d. Variado   e. Bien pagado   f. Dependiente/a   g. Agradable
h. Me gustaría ser

10. Guided translation
a. Cuando termine mis estudios   b. Un trabajo en ventas   c. Me gustaría ser   d. Un trabajo al aire libre
e. Voy a ser profesor   f. Me gustaría trabajar como   g. Un trabajo de oficina   h. Hacer trabajo voluntario

11. English to Spanish translation
a. Me gustaría trabajar como piloto porque me permite/permitirá viajar.

b. Me gustaría trabajar como profesor porque es gratificante.

c. Me gustaría ser/hacerme cirujano/a porque es un trabajo bien pagado.

d. Me gustaría ser/hacerme abogado/a porque es divertido.

e. Me gustaría un trabajo al aire libre porque me gustaría estar en contacto con la naturaleza.

f. Me gustaría trabajar de taxista porque es variado.

THE LANGUAGE GYM

Unit 8. What job I would like to do and why - Higher

1. Match

Ventas – *Sales*   Agotador – *Tiring*   En auge – *Fast-growing*   Artesano/a – *Craftsperson*
Viajar – *To travel*   Los demás – *Others*   Vendedor/a – *Sales person*   Una vez – *Once*   Como – *As*

2. Gapped translation

a. *After my* **studies**   b. *In my* **opinion**   c. *According to* my friends   d. *My parents* **tell** *me*
e. *I* **should** *do*   f. *I want* **to become**   g. *It's very* **fashionable/trendy**

3. Broken words: a. Los de**más**   b. Equi**po**   c. Esta car**rera**   d. Una indus**tria**   e. Ele**gir**   f. Ven**tas**

4. Faulty translation

a. Los trabajos de oficina: **Office** *jobs*   b. √   c. Los trabajos al aire libre*:* **Outdoor** *jobs*
d. Debería trabajar*: I should* **work**   e. Mi amigo me dice que*: My friend* **tells me** *that*
f. Mis profes piensan que*: My teachers* **think** *that*   g. Un sector en auge: *A* **fast**-*growing sector*

5. Translate into English (all sections)

a. An independent job   b. An office job   c. According to me   d. Fast-growing   e. Tiring/Exhausting   f. Outdoor
g. My friends tell me that   h. I should do medicine   i. My teachers think that   j. It seems demanding
k. To work as a team   l. A career in sales

6. Missing vowels: jobs

a. abogado/a   b. artesano/a   c. contable   d. profesor   e. informático/a   f. arquitecto/a

7. Complete with the missing word: a. trabajo   b. auge   c. muy   d. gustaría   e. en   f. termine

8. Sentence puzzle

a. La informática es un sector fascinante y que está en auge   b. A mi parecer, creo que debería ser abogado
c. Después de mis estudios, me gustaría trabajar como contable   d. Mis amigos dicen que debería tener una
carrera en ventas   e. Yo prefiero los trabajos de oficina   f. Mi hermano mayor me dice que debería trabajar
como periodista

9. Complete the table

Fast-growing: **En auge**   *I would like to be:* **Me gustaría ser**   *Office jobs:* **Los trabajos de oficina**
According to me: **A mi parecer**   *Sports instructor:* **Entrenador deportivo**   *My friends say:* **Mis amigos dicen**
Demanding: **Exigente**   *To do a career:* **Hacer una carrera**   *A manual job:* **Un trabajo manual**

10. Wordsearch

	T	R	A	B	A	J	O	I
S		E						N
E			M			D		
C				P	U		R	V
T				S	L	O		E
O			T		D	E		N
R		R		A			O	T
	I		T					A
A	L	O	S	D	E	M	Á	S
	G							
A	O	N	A	S	E	T	R	A

Tiring: **Agotador**
Employment: **Empleo**
Others: **Los demás**
Sales: **Ventas**
Sector: **Sector**
Craftsman: **Artesano/a**
Job: **Empleo/Trabajo**
Industry: **Industria**

11. Guided translation

a. Un sector en auge   b. A mi parecer   c. Me gustaría ser   d. Un trabajo de oficina   e. Me gustaría trabajar
f. Después de mis estudios   g. Trabajar en ventas   h. Me permitirá   i. Entrenador deportivo

12. Translate into Spanish

a. Después de mis estudios, me gustaría trabajar como cirujano.
b. Me gusta este trabajo, ya que me permitirá viajar.
c. Este trabajo parece exigente, pero no estresante.
d. Debería hacer una carrera en ventas.
e. Mis padres dicen que debo/debería estudiar medicina.
f. Mi hermano me dice que debo/debería trabajar como profesor/a.
g. Prefiero los trabajos al aire libre, por eso/así que me gustaría ser agricultor.
h. Este trabajo me permitirá ayudar a los demás.
i. Sueño con tener esta carrera, ya que creo que esta profesión es fascinante.

 **THE LANGUAGE GYM**

ANSWERS - UNIT 8 - Test (/100)

1. Vocabulary recognition - Spanish to English translation (/15)

a. My studies

b. Diploma

c. Plumber

d. I would like

e. A job

f. Tiring

g. I am going to be

h. Craftsman

i. Office

j. Outdoor

k. To help

l. Sales assistant

m. Exciting

n. It allows you to

o. To earn

2. Syntax/Lexicogrammar – Split sentences (/5)

Este trabajo te permite	**viajar**
Quiero trabajar	**al aire libre**
Mi trabajo me permitirá estar en	**contacto con la naturaleza**
Me gustaría ganar	**mucho dinero**
Voy a ser profesor,	**como mi padre**

3. Grammar/Morphology/Vocabulary – Tangled translation (/20)

a. Voy a ser **fontanero**

b. **Me gustaría** un trabajo **bien pagado**

c. **Según** mis **amigos/as**

d. **Quiero** hacer **este trabajo**

e. Me gustaría tener un trabajo **al aire libre**

f. Me gustaría **ser ingeniero**

g. **Prefiero** el trabajo **independiente**

h. Es una **industria que** es lucrativa

i. Me gustaría **trabajar** como **artesano**

j. Mis padre me **dicen que** debería ser médico

k. Está **de moda** en **este** momento

l. Me gustaría hacer una **carrera** en **ventas**

4. Translate into Spanish (/ 60 – each full sentence – 6 points)

a. Una vez que tenga mi título, me gustaría ser contable.

b. Me gusta esta profesión porque me permitirá viajar.

c. Mis padres dicen que debería estudiar medicina en la universidad.

d. Prefiero el trabajo independiente, así que/por eso me gustaría ser abogado.

e. Mis amigos dicen que debería intentar trabajar como entrenador deportivo.

f. Yo prefiero los trabajos al aire libre, así que podría ser agricultor.

g. En mi opinión, es un sector que está en auge en este momento.

h. A mi parecer, esta es una industria que es bastante lucrativa hoy en día.

i. Mi hermano dice que debería intentar hacer una carrera en ventas.

j. Sueño con tener esta carrera, ya que creo que esta profesión es muy gratificante.

 THE LANGUAGE GYM

Unit 9. Home, city, neighbourhood and region

KEY VOCABULARY Foundation

Las habitaciones *(rooms)*

En mi casa hay seis habitaciones:
In my house there are six rooms
-aseos: *toilets*
-un comedor: *a dining room*
-un garaje: *a garage*
-un jardín: *a garden*
-un salón: *a living room*
-una cocina: *a kitchen*
En el primer/segundo piso, hay:
On the first/second floor, there is/are
-cuatro dormitorios: *four bedrooms*
-dos cuartos de baño: *two bathrooms*
-una oficina: *an office*

Las tiendas *(shops)*

En mi ciudad/barrio, hay:
In my city/neighbourhood there is/are
-tiendas: *shops*
-centros comerciales: *malls*
-una (gran) biblioteca: *a (big) library*
-una estación de trenes: *a train station*
-una estación de autobuses: *a bus station*
-parques: *parks*
-una (gran) calle peatonal:
a (big) pedestrianised street
En mi calle, hay:
In my street, there is
-una carnicería: *a butcher's*
-una panadería: *a bakery*

Por qué (no) me gusta mi ciudad/barrio

Me gusta porque es:
I like it because it's
-bonito/a: *pretty*
-limpio/a: *clean*
-seguro/a: *safe*
-tranquilo/a: *quiet*
Hay muchas cosas que:
There are lots of things to
-hacer: *do*
-ver: *see*
No me gusta porque es:
I don't like it because it's
-peligroso/a: *dangerous*
-ruidoso/a: *noisy*
-sucio/a: *dirty*

1. Match

Hay siete habitaciones	*On the first floor*
En mi ciudad	*In my neighbourhood*
En el primer piso	*On the second floor*
En mi barrio	*On my street*
En el segundo piso	*In my city*
En mi calle	*Lots of things to do*
Muchas cosas que ver	*I like my neighbourhood*
Me gusta mi barrio	*Lots of things to see*
Muchas cosas que hacer	*There are seven rooms*

2. Gapped translation with options

a. En el ___ _____ piso: *On the second floor*

b. Hay siete _____ : *There are 7 rooms*

c. En _____ casa: *In my house*

d. Muchas _____ que hacer: *Lots of things to do*

e. En mi _____ : *In my neighbourhood*

f. En el _____ piso: *On the first floor*

g. Mi _____ está sucia: *My city is dirty*

cosas	ciudad	habitaciones	primer
barrio	segundo	mi	sucia

3. Broken words

a. Una estaci_ _ : *A station*   g. Ca _ _ _ : *Street*

b. Tranq _ _ _ _ : *Quiet*   h. Rui _ _ _ _ : *Noisy*

c. Segu_ _ : *Safe*   i. V _ _ : *To see*

d. Co_ _ _ : *Things*   j. Su _ _ _ : *Dirty*

e. Lim _ _ _ : *Clean*   k. Par _ _ _ : *Park*

f. Carnice_ _ _ : *Butcher's*   l. Bon _ _ _ : *Pretty*

4. Sentence puzzle

a. peatonal gran Una zona: *A big pedestrian area*

b. Me ciudad mi gusta: *I like my city*

c. Muchas que hacer cosas: *Lots of things to do*

d. contaminado bastante Está: *It's quite polluted*

e. es No segura: *It isn't safe*

f. el En piso primer: *On the first floor*

g. Hay habitaciones tres: *There are three rooms*

h. piso el En segundo: *On the second floor*

5. Tick the adjectives and translate them into English

a. Ático

b. Sucio

c. Piso

d. Calle

e. Contaminado

f. Bonito

g. Barrio

h. Limpio

6. Break the flow and translate into English

a. Enmipisohaysietehabitaciones: *In my flat there are 7 rooms*

b. Mihabitaciónestáenelprimerpiso:

c. Vivoenunacasagrande:

d. Megustamibarrioporqueesseguroyestálimpio:

e. Desafortunadamentemiciudadestámuycontaminada:

f. Enmiciudadhayungrancentrocomercial:

g. Megustamiciudadporquehaymuchascosasquehacer:

h. Miciudadesmuybonita:

i. Enmiciudadhaymuchascosasquever:

7. Complete the sentences

a. En el p_____ piso: *On the first floor*

b. En mi c_____ : *In my city*

c. Un c_____ : *A dining room*

d. E___ mi casa: *In my house*

e. Una zona p_____ : *A pedestrian area*

f. Hay d_____ parques: *There are two parks*

g. En mi c_____ : *In my street*

h. En mi calle hay m_____ cafés
In my street there are lots of cafés

8. Complete the table

English	Spanish
In my street	
	En mi ciudad
	Hay
On the second floor	
	Una calle peatonal
Lots of things to do	
	Es ruidoso
It is safe	
	Es tranquilo

9. Match the opposites

Limpio	**Ruidoso**
Grande	**Feo**
Seguro	**Sucio**
Tranquilo	**Nuevo**
Bonito	**Pequeño**
Viejo	**Peligroso**

10 Translate the adjectives into Spanish

a. Dirty

b. Dangerous

c. Small

d. Ugly

e. Safe

f. Clean

g. Quiet

h. New

11. Tangled translation

a. Vivo **in** una **house** vieja **in** el centro

b. Mi **neighbourhood** está **clean**

c. No me **like my** ciudad porque es **noisy**

d. En mi **city** hay **lots** cosas que **do**

e. Mi barrio también está **dirty** y **polluted**

f. **In** mi calle **there is** un centro comercial **big**

g. **I live** en un **neighbourhood** pequeño

h. En el **first** piso hay tres **rooms**

i. **On** el segundo **floor** hay cuatro habitaciones

12. Translate into Spanish

a. In my city there are lots of things to do

b. On the second floor there are five rooms

c. I live in a small house in the city centre

d. My neighbourhood is quite dirty and polluted

e. I don't like my city as it's dirty and polluted

f. I like my neighbourhood a lot because it is clean

g. On the first floor there are three rooms

h. In my city there are plenty of things to see

i. On my street there are many cafés and shops

KEY VOCABULARY Higher

1. Las habitaciones que hay en mi casa
(The rooms in my house)

En mi casa: *In my house*
En el primer/segundo piso:
On the first/second floor
hay: *there is/are*
-cinco habitaciones: *five rooms*
-dos cuartos de baño: *two bathrooms*
-tres dormitorios: *three bedrooms*
-una cocina: *a kitchen*
-un salón: *a living room*

2. Tipos de alojamiento *(accommodation)*

Vivo en: *I live in*
-un edificio: *a building/block of flats*
-un piso: *a flat*
-una casa: *a house*

3. Dónde vivo *(Where I live)*

En el campo: *In the countryside*
En el centro: *In the city center*
En la montaña: *In the mountains*
En las afueras: *In the outskirts*

4. Qué hay donde vivo
(What there is where I live)

En mi calle/barrio hay:
In my street/neighbourhood there is/are
En mi ciudad/región hay:
In my city/region there is/are
-un centro comercial: *a mall*
-un río: *a river*
-una biblioteca: *a library*
-una calle/zona peatonal:
a pedestrian street/zone
-cosas que hacer/ver para los jóvenes:
things to do/see for young people
-estaciones de esquí: *ski resorts*
-hoteles en la costa: *hotels on the coast*
-monumentos/lugares históricos:
historical monuments/places
-parques de atracciones: *amusement parks*
-playas: *beaches*
-tiendas: *shops*
-zonas verdes: *green spaces*

5. Por qué (no) me gusta mi barrio/ciudad

Porque es: *Because it's*
-bonito/a: *pretty*   - feo/a: *ugly*
-limpio/a: *clean*   - sucio/a: *dirty*
-seguro/a: *safe*   - peligroso/a: *dangerous*
-tranquilo/a: *quiet*   - ruidoso/a: *noisy*

1. Match

Tiendas	*Buildings*
Campo	*Street*
Edificios	*House*
Calle	*Floor*
Afueras	*Things*
Cosas	*City*
Barrio	*Outskirts*
Ciudad	*Neighbourhood*
Piso	*Shops*
Jóvenes	*Countryside*
Casa	*Young people*

2. Gapped translation

a. Vivo en las afueras: *I live _____*
b. Hay seis habitaciones: *There are six _____*
c. En el primer piso: *On the _____floor*
d. En mi calle: *On my _____*
e. Vivo en el campo: *I live in the _____*
f. En mi barrio: *In my _____*
g. En un edificio moderno: *In a modern _____*
h. Donde vivo: *_____ I live*
i. Hay zonas verdes: *There are _____ spaces*
j. Hay tiendas buenas: *There are _____ shops*

3. Translate into English

a. Cosas que hacer

b. Zonas verdes

c. En mi calle

d. En las afueras

e. El segundo piso

f. Un edificio viejo

g. En mi casa hay

h. Una calle peatonal

4. Broken words

a. Co_ _ : *Thing*
b. Cal_ _ : *Street*
c. R_ _ : *River*
d. Pla_ _ : *Beach*
e. Habitaci_ _ _ _ : *Rooms*
f. Tie _ _ _ : *Shop*
g.Ciu_ _ _ : *City*
h. P_ _ _ : *Flat*

5. Missing vowels (section 5)

a. R_ _d_s_
b. F_ _
c. S_c_ _
d. S_g_r
e. B_n_t_
f. L_mp_ _
g. P_l_gr_s_

THE LANGUAGE GYM

6. Choose the correct translation

a. Campo: countryside/building/flat

b. Edificio: building/lake/river

c. Piso: outskirts/neighbourhood/floor

d. Viejo: new/old/ugly

e. Afueras: outskirts/space/room

f. Habitaciones: streets/cities/rooms

7. Complete with the correct option from the box

a. Una calle _____

b. Vivo en el _____

c. Mi _____

d. _____ que hacer

e. Las zonas _____

f. Hay ocho _____

peatonal	
habitaciones	
casa	
cosas	
verdes	
campo	

8. Match the opposites

Bonito	Ruidoso
Viejo	Sucio
Tranquilo	Feo
Grande	Pobre
Peligroso	Nuevo
Limpio	Pequeño
Rico	Seguro

9. Gapped English to Spanish translation

a. Vivo en las _____ : *I live on the outskirts*

b. En mi _____ hay tiendas: *On my street there are shops*

c. Vivo en una casa _____: *I live in an old house*

d. Mi _____ es ruidoso: *My neighbourhood is noisy*

e. En el primer _____ hay 3 habitaciones: *On the 1st floor there are 3 rooms*

f. No me gusta mi _____ porque es _____ y muy pequeña:
I don't like my house because it is old and very small

g. _____ muchos _____ históricos: *There are lots of historic places*

10. Complete the table

English	Español
Places	
	Barrio
	Habitaciones
Shops	
	Ciudad
Countryside	
	Feo
Clean	
Safe	

11. Wordsearch – Find the Spanish for the listed words

M	A	N	U	L	I	C	M
N	R	U	I	D	O	S	O
Ó	R	N	E	S	P	A	R
I	A	Y	A	L	P	A	E
C	S	S	I	F	I	R	D
A	E	U	E	N	S	O	I
T	C	C	G	E	O	N	F
I	H	I	R	Ü	I	E	I
B	R	O	P	O	R	A	C
A	I	L	V	I	N	F	I
H	S	L	I	M	P	I	O

Room: H

Things: C

Dirty: S

Beach: P

Floor: P

Noisy: R

Building: E

Clean: L

12. Guided translation

a. *My city is clean*: M_ c_____ e_____ l_____

b. *My neighbourhood*: M_ b_____

c. *There are hotels*: H___ h_____

d. *I live on the outskirts*: V____ e_l__ a_____

e. *It's safe but noisy*: E_ s_____ p____ r_____

f. *Many green spaces*: M_____ z_____ v____

g. *A pedestrian area*: U___ z____ p_____

h. *My city is not safe*: M_ c_____ n_e_ s_____

i. *In my house there are seven rooms*:
En m__ c_____ h____ s_____ h_____

j. *Things to see*: C_____ q____ v_____

13. Translate into Spanish

a. My city is dirty and polluted

b. I live in an old block of flats

c. In my house there are eight rooms

d. My neighbourhood is very noisy

e. In my region there are many ski resorts

f. I live in a small house in the mountains

g. In my city there are many green spaces

h. My neighbourhood is clean and safe

UNIT 9 - Test (/100)

1. Vocabulary recognition - Spanish to English translation (/15)

a. En mi casa

b. El primer piso

c. Un comedor

d. Hay

e. El segundo piso

f. Cosas que hacer

g. En mi barrio

h. Siete habitaciones

i. Cosas que ver

j. En mi ciudad

k. En mi calle

l. Está limpia

m. Es ruidosa

n. Es peligrosa

o. Está sucia

2. Syntax/Lexicogrammar – Split sentences (/5)

En el primer piso	**tiendas en mi calle**
Vivo en	**que hacer**
No hay	**hay cuatro habitaciones**
Hay muchas cosas	**es bastante bonita**
Me gusta mi ciudad porque	**el campo**

3. Grammar/Morphology/Vocabulary – Tangled translation (/20)

a. **There are** zonas **green**

b. **In** ciudad no hay zona **pedestrian**

c. **On the** primer **floor** está mi habitación

d. En mi **street** no hay ninguna **bakery**

e. Vivo en una **old house** en las afueras

f. Hay muchos **places historic**

g. En mi barrio hay muchas cosas **to do**

h. **At home** hay siete **rooms**

i. Mi **neighbourhood** es bastante **pretty**

j. El centro es muy **noisy** y está **polluted**

k. Lo que **most** me gusta son las **shops**

l. Mi barrio es **safe** y **quiet**

4. Translate into Spanish (/ 60 – each full sentence – 6 points)

a. What I like the most about my city is the shopping mall.

b. I don't like my neighbourhood because it's dirty and dangerous.

c. I would like to live in the countryside because it's less polluted.

d. In my neighbourhood, there are not many things to do.

e. In the city centre there are many shops and cafés.

f. In my street there are a bakery, a supermarket and a gym.

g. I don't like my city because it's ugly.

h. I live in a small flat in an old building on the outskirts.

i. In my house there are five rooms. My favourite room is my bedroom.

j. I like my city because there are lots of things to do for young people.

 **THE LANGUAGE GYM**

69

ANSWERS - Unit 9. Home, city, neighbourhood and region - Foundation

1. Match
Hay siete habitaciones – ***There are seven rooms***   En mi ciudad – ***In my city***
En el primer piso – ***On the first floor***   En mi barrio – ***In my neighbourhood***
En el segundo piso – ***On the second floor***   En mi calle – ***On my street***
Muchas cosas que ver – ***Lots of things to see***   Me gusta mi barrio – ***I like my neighbourhood***
Muchas cosas que hacer – ***Lots of things to do***

2. Gapped translation with options
a. segundo   b. habitaciones   c. mi   d. cosas   e. barrio   f. primer   g. ciudad

3. Broken words
a. Una esta**ción**   b. Tran**quilo**   c. Segu**ro**   d. Co**sas**   e. Lim**pio**   f. Carnice**ría**   g. Ca**lle**   h. Rui**doso**   i. V**er**
j. Su**cio**   k. Par**que**   l. Bon**ito**

4. Sentence puzzle
a. Una gran zona peatonal   b. Me gusta mi ciudad   c. Muchas cosas que hacer
d. Está bastante contaminado   e. No es segura   f. En el primer piso
g. Hay tres habitaciones   h. En el segundo piso

5. Tick the adjectives and translate them into English
a. X   b. Sucio – Dirty   c. X   d. X   e. Contaminado – Polluted   f. Bonito – Pretty   g. X   h. Limpio – Clean

6. Break the flow and translate into English
a. En mi piso hay siete habitaciones: *In my flat there are 7 rooms*
b. Mi habitación está en el primer piso: *My room is on the first floor*
c. Vivo en una casa grande: *I live in a big house*
d. Me gusta mi barrio porque es seguro y está limpio: *I like my neighbourhood because it's safe and clean*
e. Desafortunadamente mi ciudad está muy contaminada: *Unfortunately, my city is very polluted*
f. En mi ciudad hay un gran centro comercial: *In my city there's a big mall*
g. Me gusta mi ciudad porque hay muchas cosas que hacer: *I like my city because there's lots of thing to do*
h. Mi ciudad es muy bonita: *My city is very pretty*
i. En mi ciudad hay muchas cosas que ver: *In my city there are lots of things to see*

7. Complete the sentences
a. **pri**mer   b. En mi **ciudad**   c. Un **comedor**   d. E**n** mi casa   e. Una zona **peatonal**   f. Hay d**os** parques
g. En mi **calle**   h. En mi calle hay m**uchos** cafés

8. Complete the table
In my street: **En mi calle**   *In my city:* **En mi ciudad**   *There is/are:* **Hay**
On the second floor: **En el segundo piso**   *A pedestrian street:* **Una calle peatonal**
Lots of things to do: **Muchas cosas que hacer**   *It is noisy:* **Es ruidoso**   *It is safe:* **Es seguro/a**
It is calm: **Es tranquilo**

9. Match the opposites
Limpio – Sucio   Grande – Pequeño   Seguro – Peligroso   Tranquilo – Ruidoso   Bonito – Feo   Viejo – Nuevo

10. Translate the adjectives into Spanish
a. Sucio   b. Peligroso   c. Pequeño   d. Feo   e. Seguro   f. Limpio   g. Silencioso/Tranquilo   h. Nuevo

11. Tangled translation
a. Vivo **en** una **casa** vieja **en** el centro   b. Mi **barrio** está **limpio**   c. No me **gusta mi** ciudad porque es **ruidosa**
d. En mi **ciudad** hay **muchas** cosas que **hacer**   e. Mi barrio también está **sucio** y **contaminado**
f. **En** mi calle **hay** un centro comercial **grande**   g. **Vivo** en un **barrio** pequeño
h. En el **primer** piso hay tres **habitaciones**   i. **En** el segundo **piso** hay cuatro habitaciones

12. Translate into Spanish
a. En mi ciudad hay muchas cosas que hacer   b. En el segundo piso hay cinco habitaciones
c. Vivo en una casa pequeña en el centro de la ciudad   d. Mi barrio está bastante sucio y contaminado
e. No me gusta mi ciudad porque está sucia y contaminada   f. Me gusta mucho mi barrio porque está limpio
g. En el primer piso hay tres habitaciones   h. En mi ciudad hay muchas cosas que ver
i. En mi calle hay muchas cafeterías y tiendas

THE LANGUAGE GYM

ANSWERS - Unit 9. Home, city, neighbourhood and region - Higher

1. Match

Tiendas – *Shops*   Campo – *Countryside*   Edificios – *Buildings*   Calle – *Street*   Afueras – *Outskirts*
Cosas – *Things*   Barrio – *Neighbourhood*   Ciudad – *City*   Piso – *Floor*   Jóvenes – *Young people*
Casa – *House*

2. Gapped translation

a. *in the outskirts*   b. *rooms*   c. *first*   d. *street*   e. *countryside*   f. *neighbourhood*   g. *building*   h. *Where*
i. *green* j. *good*

3. Translate into English

a. Things to do   b. Green spaces   c. In my street   d. In the outskirts
e. The second floor   f. An old building   g. In my house there is   h. A pedestrianised street

4. Broken words

a. Co**sa** b. Ca**lle** c. Rí**o** d. Pla**ya** e. Habitaci**ones** f. Tie**nda** g.Ciu**dad** h. **P**iso

5. Missing vowels (section 5)

a. R**ui**doso   b. **Fe**o   c. S**u**cio   d. Seg**u**ro   e. **Bo**nito   f. L**i**mp**io**   g. P**e**ligr**o**so

6. Choose the correct translation

a. Campo: countryside   b. Edificio: building   c. Piso: floor   d. Viejo: old   e. Afueras: outskirts
f. Habitaciones: rooms

7. Complete with the correct option from the box

a. peatonal   b. campo   c. casa   d. Cosas   e. verdes   f. habitaciones

8. Match the opposites

Bonito – Feo   Viejo – Nuevo   Tranquilo – Ruidoso   Grande – Pequeño
Peligroso – Seguro   Sucio – Limpio   Rico – Pobre

9. Gapped English to Spanish translation

a. **afueras**   b. **calle**   c. **vieja**   d. **barrio**   e. **piso**   f. **casa / vieja**   g. **Hay / lugares**

10. Complete the table

Places: **Lugares**   *Neighbourhood:* **Barrio**   *Rooms:* **Habitaciones**   *Shops:* **Tiendas**   *City:* **Ciudad**
Countryside: **Campo**   *Ugly:* **Feo**   *Clean:* **Limpio**   *Safe:* **Seguro**

11. Wordsearch

					C		
N	R	U	I	D	O	S	O
Ó			S				
I	A	Y	A	L	P		E
C		S			I		D
A		U		S			I
T		C		O			F
I		I					I
B		O					C
A							I
H		L	I	M	P	I	O

Room: **Habitación**
Things: **Cosas**
Dirty: **Sucio**
Beach: **Playa**
Floor: **Piso**
Noisy: **Ruidoso**
Building: **Edificio**
Clean: **Limpio**

12. Guided translation

a. Mi **ciudad** está **limpia**   b. Mi **barrio**   c. Hay **hoteles**   d. **Vivo** en las **afueras**   e. Es **seguro** pero **ruidoso**
f. **Muchas** zonas **verdes**   g. **Una** zona **peatonal**   h. Mi **ciudad** no es **segura**   i. En mi **casa** hay **siete**
habitaciones   j. **Cosas** que ver

13. Translate into Spanish

a. Mi ciudad está sucia y contaminada   b. Vivo en un viejo bloque de pisos
c. En mi casa casa hay ocho habitaciones   d. Mi barrio es muy ruidoso
e. En mi región hay muchas estaciones de esquí   f. Vivo en una casa pequeña en las montañas
g. En mi ciudad hay muchas zonas verdes   h. Mi barrio está limpio y es seguro

THE LANGUAGE GYM

ANSWERS - UNIT 9 - Test (/100)

1. Vocabulary recognition - Spanish to English translation (/15)

a. In my house

b. The first floor

c. A dining room

d. There is/are

e. The second floor

f. Things to do

g. In my neighbourhood

h. Seven rooms

i. Things to see

j. In my city

k. In my street

l. It's clean

m. It's noisy

n. It's dangerous

o. It's dirty

2. Syntax/Lexicogrammar – Split sentences (/5)

En el primer piso	**hay cuatro habitaciones**
Vivo en	**el campo**
No hay	**tiendas en mi calle**
Hay muchas cosas	**que hacer**
Me gusta mi ciudad porque	**es bastante bonita**

3. Grammar/Morphology/Vocabulary – Tangled translation (/20)

a. **Hay** zonas **verdes**

b. **En** ciudad no hay zona **peatonal**

c. **En el** primer **piso** está mi habitación

d. En mi **calle** no hay ninguna **panadería**

e. Vivo en una **casa vieja** en las afueras

f. Hay muchos **lugares históricos**

g. En mi barrio hay muchas cosas **que hacer**

h. **En casa** hay siete **habitaciones**

i. Mi **barrio** es bastante **bonito**

j. El centro es muy **ruidoso** y está **contaminado**

k. Lo que **más** me gusta son las **tiendas**

l. Mi barrio es **seguro** y **tranquilo**

4. Translate into Spanish (/ 60 – each full sentence – 6 points)

a. Lo que más me gusta de mi ciudad es el centro comercial.

b. No me gusta mi barrio porque está sucio y es peligroso.

c. Me gustaría vivir en el campo porque está menos contaminado.

d. En mi barrio no hay muchas cosas que hacer.

e. En el centro de la ciudad hay muchas tiendas y cafeterías.

f. En mi calle hay una panadería, un supermercado y un gimnasio.

g. No me gusta mi ciudad porque es fea.

h. Vivo en un piso pequeño en un edificio viejo en las afueras.

i. En mi casa hay cinco habitaciones. Mi habitación favorita es mi dormitorio.

j. Me gusta mi ciudad porque hay muchas cosas que hacer para los jóvenes.

THE LANGUAGE GYM

Unit 10. Travel and tourism

KEY VOCABULARY Foundation

Los países *(countries)*

El año pasado fui a: *Last year I went to*

El año próximo iré a: *Next year, I will go to*

- Alemania: *Germany*
- Escocia: *Scotland*
- España: *Spain*
- Inglaterra: *England*

El transporte

Viajé en: *I travelled by*

Viajaré en: *I will travel by*

- avión: *plane*
- barco: *boat*
- coche: *car*

El alojamiento *(accommodation)*

Me quedé / alojé en: *I stayed in*

Me quedaré / alojaré en: *I will stay in*

- un albergue juvenil: *a youth hostel*
- un camping: *a campsite*
- un hotel de 4 estrellas: *a 4-star hotel*

Lugares de interés *(places of interest)*

Visité: *I visited*

Visitaré: *I will visit*

- castillos: *castles*
- lugares históricos: *historic places*
- museos: *museums*

Otros lugares *(other places)*

Fui: *I went*

Iré: *I will go*

- a la playa: *to the beach*
- a un bar: *to a bar*
- a un parque de atracciones: *to a theme park*
- a un restaurante: *to a bar*
- a una discoteca: *to a club*

Actividades

Hice: *I did*

Haré: *I will do*

- piragüismo: *kayaking*
- submarinismo: *scuba diving*
- turismo: *sightseeing*
- visitas guiadas: *guided visits*

Adjetivos útiles

Fue: *It was*

Será: *It will be*

- divertido: *fun*
- inolvidable: *unforgettable*
- relajante: *relaxing*

1. Match

En avión	*To England*
A Alemania	*By car*
Un albergue juvenil	*To Germany*
A Inglaterra	*A youth hostel*
En barco	*To the beach*
A Escocia	*Unforgettable*
A la playa	*By plane*
En coche	*To Greece*
Inolvidable	*To Scotland*
A Grecia	*By boat*

2. Gapped translation

a. El año pasado: *Last _____*

b. A Alemania: *To _____*

c. Me alojé en: *I _____ in*

d. En avión: *By _____*

e. Lugares históricos: *Historic _____*

f. Un hotel de tres estrellas: *A _____ _____ hotel*

g. Fui en barco: *I went _____*

h. Hice submarinismo: *I went _____*

3. Broken words

a. Me que_ _ : *I stayed*

b. En un camp_ _ _: *In a campsite*

c. Fui a una disc_ _ _ _ _ : *I went to a club*

d. Me que_ _ _ _ : *I will stay*

e. A la pla_ _ : *To the beach*

f. Ha_ _ : *I will do*

g. Submar_ _ _ _ _ _ : *Scuba diving*

4. Break the flow

a. Iréalaplayatodoslosdías

b. Harésubmarinismo

c. Seráinolvidable

d. Visitarélugareshistóricos

e. ElañopasadofuiaGrecia

f. ElpróximoañoiréaItalia

g. Viajéenaviónyencoche

5. Missing vowels

a. F_ _: *I went*

b. T_r_sm_: *sightseeing*

c. G_n_ _l: *Great*

d. Pl_ _ _: *Beach*

e. D_v_rt_d_: *Fun*

f. R_l_j_nt_: *Relaxing*

g. H_r_: *I will do*

h. L_g_r_s: *Places*

i. C_st_ll_s: *Castles*

6. Complete the table

Preterite	Present	Future
	Voy	
		Haré
	Viajo	
Bebí		
	Es	
		Me alojaré
Comí		
	Compro	
		Tomaré

7. Gapped English to Spanish translation

a. _____ en avión: *I will travel by plane*

b. _____ submarinismo: *I went scuba diving*

c. Fui a la _____: *I went to the club*

d. _____ platos locales: *I ate local dishes*

e. Un hotel de cuatro _____: *A four-star hotel*

f. _____ en tren: *I will travel by train*

g. _____ genial: *It will be great*

h. _____ a la playa: *I will go to the beach*

i. Fue _____: *It was unforgettable*

j. Fui a _____: *I went to Scotland*

8. Complete the table

English	Spanish
Four-star hotel	
I will go	
	Fue inolvidable
It will be great	
	Viajaré
In Scotland	
	Hice turismo

9. Wordsearch – Find the Spanish for the listed words

M	A	E	S	C	O	C	I	A	N
I	R	N	O	R	E	N	P	R	Ó
S	A	E	L	C	O	L	O	M	I
H	C	P	L	A	Y	A	S	A	V
I	E	Y	I	H	M	I	R	É	A
K	T	N	T	O	Ü	N	S	N	S
A	O	P	S	G	I	E	U	U	A
G	C	E	A	R	T	G	A	E	R
N	S	R	C	D	I	S	U	S	A
A	I	U	S	E	R	A	G	U	L
P	D	N	G	Ü	I	N	O	E	N

Castles: C
Beach: P
Kayaking: P
Great: G
Club: D
I will go: I
Places: L
Scotland: E
Plane: A

10. Complete with the future tense

a. El próximo año i_____ a Escocia

b. (Yo) V_____ en avión y después en coche

c. Me a_____ en un hotel de cuatro estrellas

d. H_____ turismo y t_____ muchas fotos

e. C_____ en un restaurante, c_____ ropa y
v_____ museos, castillos y una catedral

f. ¡S_____ genial!

11. Translate into Spanish

a. I will eat

b. It was unforgettable

c. I will go

d. I will visit

e. I will be

f. It will be great

g. I will go clubbing

12. Translate into Spanish

a. Last year I went to Spain

b. I travelled by plane and then by car

c. Next year, I will go to France

d. I will travel by train, then by bike

e. I will stay in a youth hostel

f. I will do a lot of things

g. I will go sightseeing and take a lot of photos

h. I visited a lot of historic places

i. It was relaxing and truly unforgettable

j. I stayed in a four-star hotel

k. I went swimming and scuba diving

l. Next summer, I will stay in a youth hostel

m. I will eat local food and will go clubbing

n. I will go to the beach. It will be great

THE LANGUAGE GYM

KEY VOCABULARY Higher
1. Los países que visité y que visitaré
Fui / Iré: *I went / I will go*
-a Portugal: *to Portugal*
-a los Estados Unidos: *to the United States*
-a Alemania: *to Germany*
2. Cómo viajé y viajaré
Viajé / Viajaré: *I travelled / I will travel*
-en autocar: *by coach*
-en avión: *by plane*
-en barco: *by boat*
Alquilé / Alquilaré: *I rented / I will rent*
-una bici: *a bike*
-un coche: *a car*
3. Dónde pasé / pasaré mis vacaciones
Me alojé / Me alojaré en:
I stayed / I will stay in
-un albergue juvenil: *a youth hostel*
-un hotel de tres/cuatro/cinco estrellas
a 3/4/5 star hotel
-en el campo: *in the countryside*
-en la costa: *on the coast*
-en la montaña: *in the mountains*
4. Cuánto tiempo me quedé/me quedaré
Pasé / Pasaré: *I spent / I will spend*
-cinco días: *five days*
-una semana: *one week*
-todo el verano: *all summer*
5. Actividades
Por la mañana: *In the morning*
Por la tarde: *In the afternoon*
Por la noche: *In the evening*
Todos los días: *Every day*
Hice / Haré: *I did / I will do*
-natación: *swimming*
-submarinismo: *scuba diving*
-turismo: *sightseeing*
-visitas guiadas: *guided visits*
Comí / Comeré en un restaurante:
I ate/I will eat in a restaurant
Salí / Saldré:
I went out / I will go out
Fui / Iré de marcha: *I went/will go clubbing*
Fui / Iré de tiendas: *I went/will go shopping*
Visité / Visitaré
I visited / I will visit
-lugares históricos/conocidos:
historic/well-known places
6. Cómo fue / Cómo será
Fue/Será: *It was/It will be*
-genial: *great*
-horrible: *horrible*
-interesante: *interesting*
-relajante: *relaxing*

1. Match

Verano	*Stars*
Iré	*Winter*
Invierno	*I will rent*
Por la mañana	*A week*
Una semana	*Countryside*
Pasaré	*I spent*
Estrellas	*I rented*
Alquilé	*In the morning*
Fui	*I will go*
El campo	*I will rent*
Pasé	*I will spend*
Alquilaré	*Summer*

2. Gapped translation

a. Iré al campo: *I will go to the* _____

b. En la montaña: *In the* _____

c. Un hotel de cuatro estrellas: *A* _____ *hotel*

d. Hice natación: *I* _____

e. Haré submarinismo: *I will do* _____

f. Alquilé una bici: *I* _____ *a bike*

g. Pasé una semana allí: *I spent* _____ *there*

h. Fui en barco: *I went* _____

i. Por la tarde saldré: *In the evening, I*_____

j. Viajaré en coche: *I* _____ *by car*

3. Translate into English

a. Fui de compras

b. Pasé todo el verano

c. Me alojé en un albergue juvenil

d. Visité lugares históricos

e. Será genial

f. Fui a la playa

g. Hice turismo

h. Tomé fotos

4. Broken words

a. Maña_ _ : *Morning*

b. Ver_ _ _ : *Summer*

c. Gen_ _ _ : *Great*

d. Pla_ _ : *Beach*

e. D_ _ _ : *Days*

f. Tie_ _ _ _ : *Shops*

g. Coc_ _ : *Car*

h. Auto_ _ _ : *Coach*

5. Missing vowels (section 5)

a. M_nt_ñ_

b. C_mp_

c. _v__n

d. S_bm_r_n_sm_

e. T_rd_

f. C_st_

g. S_ldr_

6. Choose the correct translation

a. Campo: *countryside / week / plane*

b. Pasar: *to spend / to rent / to stay*

c. Lugares: *stars / places / swimming*

d. Alquilar: *to spend / to stay / to rent*

e. Estrellas: *youngsters / stars / visits*

f. Alojarse: *to go / to stay / to rent*

7. Complete with the correct option from the box

a. Pasaré una _____

b. Hice _____

c. Un albergue _____

d. Viajaré en _____

e. Hice visitas _____

f. Hice _____

| turismo |
| submarinismo |
| juvenil |
| coche |
| guiadas |
| semana |

8. Break the flow

a. ElañopasadofuiaPortugal

b. Viajéenaviónyluegoalquiléuncoche

c. Mealojéenunhotelenlacosta

d. Porlamañanafuialaplaya.Fuerelajante

e. Comíenelrestaurantedelhotel

f. Porlatardehicesubmarinismo

g. Tambiénfuidecomprasehiceturismo

h. Porlanochesalíconmihermano

9. Split sentences

Fui a	una semana
Me alojé	lugares históricos
Pasé	a Alemania
Hice	en un hotel
Fui	a las cartas
Visité	turismo
Jugué	Portugal

10. Complete the table

Español	English
	I will rent
Alquilé	
	I will spend
Pasé	
	I stayed
Me alojaré	
	I did
Haré	
	I will visit

11. Wordsearch – Find the Spanish for the listed words

M	I	P	O	A	C	F	O
R	R	E	P	R	O	E	M
O	S	O	M	A	L	S	S
H	O	L	A	C	A	T	I
A	E	H	C	O	C	R	N
C	D	O	R	M	I	E	I
É	R	P	N	E	R	L	R
R	A	L	I	U	Q	L	A
A	T	N	E	L	S	A	M
H	R	L	G	O	I	S	B
A	E	O	F	Ü	E	N	U
C	P	A	S	A	R	O	S

Diving: S

Evening: T

I will do: H

To rent: A

Car: C

Countryside: C

Stars: E

To spend: P

12. Guided translation

a. *In the morning*: P_ _ la m_ _ _ _ _ _

b. *I went clubbing*: F_ _ d_ m_ _ _ _ _

c. *Historic places*: L_ _ _ _ _ _ h_ _ _ _ _ _ _ _

d. *I did sightseeing*: H_ _ _ t_ _ _ _ _ _

e. *I spent a week*: P_ _ _ u_ _ s_ _ _ _ _

f. *I will visit*: V_ _ _ _ _ _ _

g. *On the coast*: E_ l_ c_ _ _ _

h. *I will swim*: H_ _ _ n_ _ _ _ _ _ _

i. *It will be great*: S_ _ _ _ g_ _ _ _ _

j. *It will be relaxing*: S_ _ _ r_ _ _ _ _ _ _ _

k. *I will spend*: P_ _ _ _ _

l. *I will go to Spain*: I_ _ a E_ _ _ _ _

13. Translate into Spanish

a. I stayed in a three-star hotel on the coast

b. I travelled by train and then I rented a car

c. In the morning, I went to the beach and then I did some sightseeing

d. I visited a lot of historic places and museums

e. I will do scuba diving. It will be great!

f. I will spend two weeks there

g. It was very interesting and relaxing

h. In the evening, I went clubbing with my older brother

UNIT 10 - Test (/100)

1. Vocabulary recognition – Spanish to English translation (/15)

a. Viajaré

b. Alemania

c. Luego

d. Pasaré

e. Un albergue juvenil

f. Viajé

g. En avión

h. Un coche

i. En la costa

j. Días

k. Durante

l. Este año

m. El verano

n. Al campo

o. En coche

2. Syntax/Lexicogrammar – Split sentences (/5)

Todos los días hice	**la playa**
Comí	**lugares históricos**
Tomé el sol en	**visitas guiadas**
Visité muchos	**en un albergue juvenil**
Me alojé	**en el restaurante**

3. Grammar/Morphology/Vocabulary – Tangled translation (/20)

a. Pasé dos **weeks** en **Germany**

b. **I visited places** históricos

c. **It was** muy **interesting**

d. **In the afternoon** tomé el **sun** en la playa

e. Fue **really** divertido y **relaxing**

f. **I will spend** cinco días en el **countryside**

g. **During** las **holidays** iré a Grecia

h. Por navidad **I will go to** Francia

i. ¡Será **great!**

j. **In the** tarde **I went out** con mis amigos

k. Me **will stay** en un hotel de cuatro **stars**

l. **I will do** submarinismo

4. Translate into Spanish (/ 60 – each full sentence – 6 points)

a. Last year, in the summer, I went to Spain.

b. I travelled by plane and then I rented a car.

c. We stayed in a five-star hotel on the coast.

d. We spent one week there. It was very fun.

e. I stayed in a five-star hotel in the countryside.

f. I did sightseeing and I took many pictures.

g. There were many things to do and many places to see.

h. Next year, I will go to Germany. I will travel by plane.

i. I will stay in a youth hostel in Berlin.

j. I will visit historic places and well-known monuments. It will be great!

THE LANGUAGE GYM

ANSWERS - Unit 10. Travel and tourism - Foundation

1. Match
En avión – **By plane**   En barco – **By boat**   Inolvidable – **Unforgettable**   A Alemania – **To Germany**
A Escocia – **To Scotland**   A Grecia – **To Greece**   Un albergue juvenil – **A youth hostel**
A la playa – **To the beach**   A Inglaterra – **To England**   En coche – **By car**

2. Gapped translation
a. *Last **year***   b. *To **Germany***   c. *I **stayed** in*   d. *By **plane***   e. *Historic **places***   f. *A **3-star** hotel*
g. *I went **by boat***   h. *I went **scuba diving***

3. Broken words
a. Me que**dé**   b. En un camp**ing**   c. Fui a una dis**coteca**   d. Me que**daré**   e. A la pla**ya**   f. Har**é**
g. Submar**inismo**

4. Break the flow
a. Iré a la playa todos los días   b. Haré submarinismo   c. Será inolvidable   d. Visitaré lugares históricos
e. El año pasado fui a Grecia   f. El próximo año iré a Italia   g. Viajé en avión y en coche

5. Missing vowels (section 5)
a. **Fui**   b. **Turismo**   c. **Genial**   d. **Playa**   e. **Divertido**   f. **Relajante**   g. **Haré**   h. **Lugares**   i. **Castillos**

6. Complete the table
Fui/Voy/Iré   Hice/Hago/Haré   Viajé/Viajo/Viajaré   Bebí/Bebo/Beberé   Fui/Es/Seré
Me alojé/Me alojo/Me alojaré   Comí/Como/Comeré   Compré/Compro/Compraré   Tomé/Tomo/Tomaré

7. Gapped English to Spanish translation
a. viajaré   b. hice   c. discoteca   d. comí   e. estrellas   f. viajaré   g. será   h. iré   i. inolvidable
j. Escocia

8. Complete the table
Four-star hotel: **Un hotel de cuatro estrellas**   *I will go:* **Iré**   *It was unforgettable:* **Fue inolvidable**
It will be great: **Será genial**   *I will travel:* **Viajaré**   *In Scotland:* **En Escocia**   *I did sightseeing:* **Hice turismo**

9. Wordsearch

		E	S	C	O	C	I	A	N
		O							Ó
	A	L			L		M	I	
	C	P	L	A	Y	A	S		V
	E	I			I	R	É	A	
	T	T		Ü	N				
	O	S	G		E				
	C	A			G				
	S	R	C						
	I		S	E	R	A	G	U	L
P	D								

Castles: **Castillos**
Beach: **Playas**
Kayaking: **Piragüismo**
Great: **Genial**
Club: **Discoteca**
I will go: **Iré**
Places: **Lugares**
Scotland: **Escocia**
Plane: **Avión**

10. Complete with the future tense
a. **iré**   b. **viajaré**   c. me a**lojaré**   d. h**aré** / **tomaré**   e. **comeré** / **compraré** / **visitaré**   f. **será**

11. Translate into Spanish
a. Comeré   b. Fue inolvidable   c. Iré   d. Visitaré   e. Seré   f. Será genial   g. Iré a la discoteca

12. Translate into Spanish
a. El año pasado fui a España
b. Viajé en avión y luego en coche
c. El año que viene iré a Francia
d. Viajaré en tren y luego en bici
e. Me alojaré en un albergue juvenil
f. Haré muchas cosas
g. Haré turismo y tomaré muchas fotos

h. Visité muchos lugares históricos
i. Fue relajante y verdaderamente inolvidable
j. Me alojé en un hotel de cuatro estrellas
k. Hice natación y submarinismo
l. El verano que viene me alojaré en un albergue juvenil
m. Comeré platos locales e iré de marcha
n. Iré a la playa. Será genial.

ANSWERS - Unit 10. Travel and tourism - Higher

1. Match

Verano – ***Summer***   Iré - ***I will go***   Invierno – ***Winter***   **Por la mañana** – *In the morning*

Una semana – ***A week***   Pasaré – ***I will spend***   Estrellas – ***Stars***   Alquilé – ***I rented***

Fui – ***I went***   El campo – ***Countryside*** Pasé – ***I spent***   Alquilaré – ***I will rent***

2. Gapped translation

a. *countryside*   b. *mountain(s)*   c. *four-star*   d. *did/went swimming*   e. *scuba-diving*   f. *rented*

g. *one week*   h. *by boat*   i. *I will go out*   j. *I will travel*

3. Translate into English

a. I went shopping   b. I spent all summer   c. I stayed at a youth hostel   d. I visited historic places

e. It will be great   f. I went to the beach   g. I did/went sightseeing   h. I took pictures

4. Broken words

a. Mañana   b. Verano   c. Genial   d. Playa   e. Días   f. Tiendas   g. Coche   h. Autocar

5. Missing vowels (section 5)

a. Montaña   b. Campo   c. Avión   d. Submarinismo   e. Tarde   f. Costa   g. Saldré

6. Choose the correct translation

a. *countryside*   b. *to spend*   c. *places*   d. *to rent*   e. *stars*   f. *to stay*

7. Complete with the correct option from the box

a. semana   b. submarinismo   c. juvenil   d. coche   e. guiadas   f. turismo

8. Break the flow

a. El año pasado fui a Portugal   b. Viajé en avión y luego alquilé un coche   c. Me alojé en un hotel en la costa

d. Por la mañana fui a la playa. Fue relajante.   e. Comí en el restaurante del hotel

f. Por la tarde hice submarinismo   g. También fui de compras e hice turismo   h. Por la noche salí con mi hermano

9. Split sentences

Fui a **Portugal**   Me alojé **en un hotel**   Pasé **una semana**   Hice **turismo**   Fui **a Alemania**

Visité **lugares históricos**   Jugué **a las cartas**

10. Complete the table

Alquilaré: *I will rent*   **Alquilé**: *I rented*   **Pasaré**: *I will spend*   **Pasé**: *I spent*   **Me alojé**: *I stayed*

Me alojaré: *I will stay*   **Hice**: *I did*   **Haré**: *I will do*   **Visitaré**: *I will visit*

11. Wordsearch

			O				O
			P			E	M
			M			S	S
			A			T	I
	E	H	C	O	C	R	N
	D					E	I
É	R					L	R
R	A	L	I	U	Q	L	A
A	T					A	M
H						S	B
							U
	P	A	S	A	R		S

Diving: **Submarinismo**

Evening: **Tarde**

I will do: **Haré**

To rent: **Alquilar**

Car: **Coche**

Countryside: **Campo**

Stars: **Estrellas**

To spend: **Pasar**

12. Guided translation

a. **Por la mañana**   b. **Fui de marcha**   c. **Lugares históricos**   d. **Hice turismo**   e. **Pasé una semana**

f. **Visitaré**   g. **En la costa**   h. **Haré natación**   i. **Será genial**   j. **Será relajante**   k. **Pasaré**   l. **Iré a España**

13. Translate into Spanish

a. Me alojé en un hotel de tres estrellas en la costa   b. Viajé en tren y luego alquilé un coche

c. Por la mañana fui a la playa y después hice turismo   d. Visité muchos lugares históricos y museos

e. Haré submarinismo. ¡Será genial!   f. Pasaré dos semanas allí

g. Fue muy interesante y relajante   h. Por la tarde fui de marcha con mi hermano mayor

ANSWERS - UNIT 10 - Test (/100)

1. Vocabulary recognition – Spanish to English translation (/15)

a. I will travel

b. Germany

c. Then

d. I will spend

e. A youth hostel

f. I traveled

g. By plane

h. A car

i. By the sea/On the coast

j. Days

k. During

l. This year

m. The summer

n. To the countryside

o. By car

2. Syntax/Lexicogrammar – Split sentences (/5)

Todos los días hice	**visitas guiadas**
Comí	**en el restaurante**
Tomé el sol en	**la playa**
Visité muchos	**lugares históricos**
Me alojé	**en un albergue juvenil**

3. Grammar/Morphology/Vocabulary – Tangled translation (/20)

a. Pasé dos **semanas** en **Alemania**

b. **Visité lugares** históricos

c. **Fue** muy **interesante**

d. **Por la tarde** tomé el **sol** en la playa

e. Fue **realmente** divertido y **relajante**

f. **Pasaré** cinco días en el **campo**

g. **Durante** las **vacaciones** iré a Grecia

h. Por navidad **iré a** Francia

i. ¡Será **genial**!

j. **Por la** tarde **salí** con mis amigos

k. Me **alojaré** en un hotel de cuatro **estrellas**

l. **Haré** submarinismo

4. Translate into Spanish (/ 60 – each full sentence – 6 points)

a. El año pasado, en verano, fui a España.

b. Viajé en avión y después alquilé un coche.

c. Nos alojamos en un hotel de cinco estrellas en la costa.

d. Pasamos una semana allí. Fue muy divertido.

e. Me alojé/quedé en un hotel de cinco estrellas en el campo.

f. Hice turismo y saqué/tomé muchas fotos.

g. Había muchas cosas que hacer y muchos lugares que ver.

h. El próximo año iré a Alemania. Viajaré en avión.

i. Me alojaré en un albergue juvenil en Berlín.

j. Visitaré lugares históricos y monumentos conocidos. ¡Será genial!

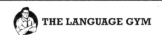 THE LANGUAGE GYM

Unit 11. Sport

KEY VOCABULARY Foundation

Los deportes de pelota *(ball sports)*
Jugué: *I played*
Juego: *I play*
Jugaré: *I will play*
-al baloncesto: *basketball*
-al fútbol: *football*
-al ping pong: *table tennis*

Otros deportes y actividades
Hice: *I did*
Hago: *I do*
Haré: *I will do*
-atletismo: *athletics*
-boxeo: *boxing*
-ciclismo: *cycling*
-culturismo: *bodybuilding*
-footing: *jogging*
-natación: *swimming*
-vela: *sailing*

Si pudiera *(If I could)*
Si pudiera, me gustaría probar :
If I could, I would like to try
-la escalada: *climbing*
-el esquí: *skiing*
-el parapente: *paragliding*
-el patinaje sobre hielo: *ice skating*
-el submarinismo: *scuba diving*

Expresiones de tiempo *(time)*
Después del colegio: *After school*
Los fines de semana: *At the weekend*
Todos los sábados: *Every Saturday*
Una vez a la semana: *Once a week*

Lugares *(places)*
Lo hago: *I do it/that*
-en casa: *at home*
-en el estadio: *at the stadium*
-en el gimnasio: *at the gym*
-en la piscina: *at the swimming pool*

¿Cómo es? *(What is it like?)*
Me parece: *I find it*
-arriesgado: *risky*
-competitivo: *competitive*
-divertido: *fun*
-emocionante: *exciting*
-entretenido: *entertaining*

1. Match

Culturismo	*Skating*
Natación	*Climbing*
Submarinismo	*Swimming*
Escalada	*Scuba diving*
Patinaje	*Boxing*
Vela	*Bodybuilding*
Boxeo	*Skiing*
Ciclismo	*Sailing*
Esquí	*Cycling*

3. Gapped translation

a. Me gustaría probar:
I would like to _____

b. Una vez a la semana:
Once a _____

c. Haré boxeo:
I will do _____

d. Si pudiera, me gustaría probar:
_____, I would like to try

e. Hago vela: *I do _____*

f. Hice ciclismo: *I did _____*

g. Lo hago en la piscina:
I do this at the _____

2. Translate into English

a. Escalada

b. Ciclismo

c. Vela

d. Submarinismo

e. Parapente

f. Patinaje sobre hielo

g. Culturismo

4. Missing vowels

a. L_ _sc_l_d_

b. _l c_lt_r_s m_

c. _l s_bm_r_n_sm_

d. _l p_r_p_nt_

e. L_ p_sc_n_

f. _l g_mn_s__

g. _l _st_d__

h. _l f__t_ng

5. Correct the wrong translations and tick the correct ones

a. La escalada: *Skiing*
b. Agotador: *Entertaining*
c. Divertido: *Boring*
d. Sábado: *Saturday*
e. El patinaje: *Diving*
f. La piscina: *Gym*
g. Emocionante: *Exciting*
h. Si pudiera: *If I did*
i. Probar: *To buy*
j. La vela: *Boxing*
k. El footing: *Jogging*
l. Lo hago: *I try that*

6. Broken words

a. Es un deporte compet_ _ _ _ _
b. Una vez a la se_ _ _ _
c. Lo ha_ _
d. Es arri_ _ _ _ _ _
e. Hago sub_ _ _ _ _ _ _ _ _
f. Es agot_ _ _ _
g. Hago esca_ _ _ _
h. Es entret_ _ _ _ _
i. Es div_ _ _ _ _ _
j. El _at__aje s__re hie__

7. Break the flow

a. Megustalanataciónporqueesrelajante

b. Hagoejercicioencasatresvecesalasemana

c. Nohagodeporteporqueesagotador

d. Juegoalrugbyyalfútboltodoslosdías

e. Hagociclismotodoslosdíasdespuésdelcolegio

f. Megustaríaprobarelparapenteporqueesarriesgado

g. Nomegustamontaracaballoporqueesaburrido

h. Elrugbymepareceemocionanteporqueescompetitivo

8. Complete with the missing words

a. Me gustaría _____ escalada

b. Este deporte me _____ emocionante

c. _____ ciclismo todos los días

d. No ___ gusta _____ al rugby

e. Ayer _____ al fútbol

f. No _____ a hacer culturismo porque _____ agotador

voy	hago	jugué	jugar
es	hacer	parece	me

9. Wordsearch – Find the Spanish for the listed words

E	N	D	A	D	A	L	A	C	S	E
T	A	B	U	R	R	I	D	O	J	P
N	G	R	B	O	L	E	S	A	R	E
A	O	A	J	A	P	Y	N	R	O	G
N	T	R	O	S	Y	I	L	I	N	R
O	A	I	V	M	T	B	L	O	G	A
I	D	V	N	A	S	O	N	T	A	B
C	O	M	P	E	T	I	T	I	V	O
O	R	E	N	G	I	B	L	Ü	L	R
M	A	D	I	H	A	R	A	C	G	P
E	R	A	N	C	A	A	T	L	I	N
F	O	M	S	I	R	U	T	L	U	C
A	R	R	I	E	S	G	A	D	O	P

Bodybuilding: C

Cycling: C

Skating: P

Climbing: E

Exciting: E

Tiring: A

Risky: A

Competitive: C

To try: P

Boring: A

10. Translate into Spanish

a. Risky

b. Bodybuilding

c. I am going to do

d. If I could

e. I would like to try

f. Exciting

g. It's competitive

h. Scuba diving

11. Gapped English-to-Spanish translation

a. Me gusta la _____ porque me_____ _____: *I like climbing because I find it exciting*

b. Hago _____ en el _____ tres veces a la _____: *I do bodybuilding in the gym 3 times a week*

c. No hago ningún _____ porque es _____: *I don't do any sport because it's tiring*

d. _____ al tenis y al _____ todos los _____: *I play tennis and football every Sunday*

e. Hago _____ todos los días _____ del colegio: *I go cycling every day after school*

f. Me gustaría _____ el parapente, ya que es_____: *I'd like to try paragliding as it's risky*

g. No me gusta la _____ ya que es _____ y _____: *I don't like sailing as it's boring and horrible*

h. El rugby me _____ emocionante y _____: *I find rugby exciting and competitive*

12. Translate into Spanish

a. I do bodybuilding at home every day

b. I like football because it's exciting

c. I play tennis three times a week

d. I don't like swimming because it's tiring

e. I don't like sailing because it's boring

f. I do jogging every Saturday because it's relaxing

g. I'd like to try paragliding because it's risky

THE LANGUAGE GYM

KEY VOCABULARY Higher

Los deportes que hago

Hago: *I do*

-atletismo: *athletics*

-ciclismo: *cycling*

-culturismo: *bodybuilding*

-footing: *jogging*

-natación: *swimming*

-vela: *sailing*

Juego: *I play*

-al baloncesto/fútbol: *basketball/ football*

Siempre gano/pierdo: *I always win/lose*

Por qué (no) me gustan ciertos deportes

Porque es: *Because it's*

-agotador: *tiring*

-arriesgado: *risky*

-competitivo: *competitive*

-emocionante: *exciting*

-entretenido: *entertaining*

Cuándo hago deporte *(when)*

Después del colegio: *After school*

Todos los sábados: *Every Saturday*

Una vez a la semana: *Once a week*

Los lugares donde hago deporte *(places)*

Lo hago: *I do it*

-en el estadio: *at the stadium*

-en el gimnasio: *at the gym*

-en la piscina: *at the swimming pool*

-en el polideportivo: *at the sports centre*

Qué deporte hice ayer

Ayer hice ciclismo:
Yesterday I did cycling

El fin de semana pasado jugué al fútbol:
Last weekend, I played football

Qué deporte haré mañana

El fin de semana próximo jugaré al golf:
Next weekend, I will play golf

Mañana haré natación:
Tomorrow, I will do swimming

Qué deporte me gustaría hacer

Si pudiera, me gustaría probar:
If I could, I would like to try

-el parapente: *paragliding*

-el patinaje sobre hielo: *ice skating*

-el submarinismo: *scuba diving*

1. Match

Hago ciclismo	*I did sailing*
Hice vela	*I played basketball*
Jugaré al balonceso	*I do jogging*
Hice ciclismo	*I will do jogging*
Haré footing	*I did bodybuilding*
Haré vela	*I did cycling*
Juego al baloncesto	*I will do cycling*
Haré ciclismo	*I will play basketball*
Hago footing	*I do cycling*
Jugué al baloncesto	*I play basketball*
Hice culturismo	*I went jogging*
Hice footing	*I will do sailing*

2. Broken words

a. Agot_ _ _ _ : *Tiring*

b. Arries_ _ _ _ : *Risky*

c. Foo_ _ _ _ : *Jogging*

d. Est_ _ _ _ : *Stadium*

e. Pisc_ _ _ : *Pool*

f. Bicicl_ _ _ : *Bicycle*

g. Mañ_ _ _ : *Tomorrow*

h. V_ _ _ : *Sailing*

i. Lu_ _ _ _ _ : *Places*

3. Translate into English

a. Divertido

b. Arriesgado

c. La vela

d. Una vez

e. Si pudiera

f. Probar

g. Haré

h. Agotador

i. Parapente

4. Gapped translation

a. Ayer hice ciclismo: *I _____ cycling yesterday*

b. Jugaré al baloncesto: *I _____ basketball*

c. Mañana haré patinaje: *_____ I will skate tomorrow*

d. Perdí el partido: *I _____ the match*

e. Haré deporte: *I _____ do sport*

f. Me gustaría probar: *I would like to _____*

g. Iré a la piscina: *I _____ to the swimming pool*

h. Hice submarinismo: *I _____ scuba diving*

5. Correct the wrong translations. Some are correct!

a. El submarinismo: *Swimming*

b. El ciclismo: *Sailing*

c. Gané: *I won*

d. El footing: *Cycling*

e. Jugaré: *I played*

f. El estadio: *Stadium*

g. Sábado: *Sunday*

h. Probar: *To like*

i. Una vez: *One game*

j. Si pudiera: *If I can*

6. Break the flow

a. Lohagoenlapiscinaunavezalasemana

b. Sipudieramegustaríaprobarelparapente

c. Ayerjuguéaltenisconmihermanoygané

d. Elfindesemanaquevieneharéculturismo

e. Misdeportesfavoritossonlaescaladayelgolf

f. Megustaríaprobarelsubmarinismo

g. Elsubmarinismoesundeportefascinante

h. Normalmenteentrenodosvecesalasemana

7. Fill the gaps with the correct options

a. El fin de _____ próximo, haré _____

b. Ayer _____ al baloncesto con mis amigos

c. Si _____, me gustaría _____ el golf

d. ¡El parapente es _____ difícil!

e. _____ dos_____ a la semana

f. Por lo _____, no _____ deporte

pudiera	entreno	demasiado	semana	probar
general	jugué	ciclismo	veces	hago

8. Wordsearch – Find the Spanish for the listed words

E	N	U	N	L	U	G	A	R	D	E	L	M	A	N
C	H	A	A	R	E	I	D	U	P	I	S	E	D	E
C	U	Y	O	A	N	O	M	B	R	E	N	G	O	E
Q	U	I	E	B	R	H	O	A	E	C	O	U	R	T
A	R	M	E	O	N	A	O	H	F	A	M	S	U	N
C	H	O	É	R	A	G	U	J	I	T	I	T	E	A
M	P	R	O	P	V	O	I	V	E	I	A	A	U	N
C	A	B	A	L	I	L	E	R	R	O	H	R	I	I
H	D	A	L	G	O	N	C	R	O	E	N	Í	U	C
C	I	N	O	D	A	G	S	E	I	R	R	A	N	S
O	N	C	I	N	R	Ü	I	N	C	H	F	M	E	A
S	O	P	E	R	E	Z	O	S	O	R	O	I	R	F

I will do: H

I will play: J

I did: H

To try: P

If I could: S

I would like: M

I do: H

I prefer: P

Fascinating: F

9. Tangled translation

a. Normalmente, **I train** dos **times** a la semana

b. El fin de semana **next** voy a **play** al bádminton

c. Mi deporte **favourite** es la escalada porque es **risky**

d. Si **could**, **I would like** probar el **scuba diving**

e. Prefiero los **sports** en **team**, ya que son más **competitive**

f. **Yesterday**, hice **sailing** y fue **great**

g. **Never** juego al golf porque es **too** difícil

10. Translate into English

a. Genial

b. Probar

c. Arriesgado

d. Parapente

e. Equipo

f. Culturismo

g. Agotador

11. Guided translation

a. *I never play*: N_____ j_____

b. *If I could*: S__ p_____

c. *I will play football*: J_____ al f_____

d. *It's more competitive*: E__ m___ c_____

e. *It's exciting*: E__ e_____

f. *I would like to try*: M_ g_____ p_____

g. *I train twice*: E_____ d____ v_____

h. *It seems fun to me*: M__ p_____ d_____

i. *I always win*: S_____ g_____

12. Translate into Spanish

a. Yesterday, I played tennis and I lost

b. My favourite sport is athletics. It's fun!

c. I would like to try rock climbing as it's risky

d. I never play golf because it seems boring to me

e. I prefer team sports because they are more fun

f. Tomorrow, I will do bodybuilding with my sister

g. In the morning, I usually go jogging alone

h. Once a week, I play basketball at school

 THE LANGUAGE GYM

UNIT 11 - Test (/100)

1. Vocabulary recognition - Spanish-to-English translation (/15)

a. Un deporte en equipo

b. Normalmente

c. Dos veces

d. Semana

e. Siempre gano

f. Ayer

g. De vez en cuando

h. La piscina

i. Divertido

j. La escalada

k. Genial

l. Hice

m. El submarinismo

n. Una hora

o. Probar

2. Syntax/Lexicogrammar – Split sentences (/5)

Entreno dos veces	**deporte**
Prefiero los deportes	**al ping pong**
No hago mucho	**hice vela**
Ayer jugué	**a la semana**
La semana pasada	**de equipo**

3. Grammar/Morphology/Vocabulary – Tangled translation (/20)

a. Todos los **Saturdays** hago **sailing**

b. **I prefer** los deportes **individual**

c. **I train** dos veces a la **week**

d. **I played** al ping pong y **it was** divertido

e. El fin de semana **last** hice **boxing**

f. **Yesterday**, jugué al tenis y **I won**

g. Mañana **I will play** al bádminton con mi **brother**

h. En general, entreno **twice a week**

i. **I go** a la **swimming pool** todos los domingos

j. **Tomorrow**, **I will do** vela con mis amigos

k. **My** deporte **favourite** es la escalada

l. **It's a sport** un poco **risky**

4. Translate into Spanish (/ 60 – each full sentence – 6 points)

a. I love ball sports like football and basketball.

b. I can't stand team sports because they are boring.

c. If I could, I would like to try rock climbing.

d. I swim at the swimming pool four times a week.

e. From time to time, I do bodybuilding. I do it at home.

f. I would like to try paragliding because it's risky.

g. I go to the gym and to the stadium once a week with my younger sister.

h. A sport that I really dislike is jogging. It's too tiring.

i. Tomorrow I will play tennis with my older brother.

j. Yesterday I did sailing with my friend, it was fun.

 THE LANGUAGE GYM

ANSWERS - Unit 11. Sport - Foundation

1. Match
Culturismo – ***Bodybuilding*** Natación – ***Swimming*** Submarinismo – ***Scuba diving*** Escalada – ***Climbing***
Patinaje – ***Skating*** Vela – ***Sailing*** Boxeo – ***Boxing*** Ciclismo – ***Cycling*** Esquí – ***Skiing***

2. Translate into English
a. *climbing* b. *cycling* c. *sailing* d. *scuba diving* e. *paragliding* f. *ice skating* g. *bodybuilding*

3. Gapped translation
a. *try* b. *week* c. *boxing* d. *If I could* e. *sailing* f. *cycling* g. *swimming pool*

4. Missing vowels
a. La escalada b. El culturismo c. El submarinismo d. El parapente e. La piscina f. El gimnasio
g. El estadio h. El footing

5. Correct the wrong translations and tick the correct ones
a. La escalada: ***Climbing*** b. Agotador: ***Tiring*** c. Divertido: ***Entertaining*** d. √ e. El patinaje: ***Skating***
f. La piscina: ***Swimming pool*** g. √ h. *If I could* i. Probar: *To* ***try*** j. La vela: ***Sailing*** k. √ l. Lo hago: *I do it*

6. Broken words
a. compet**itivo** b. sem**ana** c. Lo ha**go** d. Es arri**esgado** e. Hago sub**marinismo** f. Es agot**ador**
g. Hago esca**lada** h. Es entre**tenido** i. Es div**ertido** j. El **patin**aje s**obre hie**lo

7. Break the flow
a. Me gusta la natación porque es relajante b. Hago ejercicio en casa tres veces a la semana
c. No hago deporte porque es agotador d. Juego al rugby y al fútbol todos los días
e. Hago ciclismo todos los días después del colegio f. Me gustaría probar el parapente porque es arriesgado
g. No me gusta montar a caballo porque es aburrido h. El rugby me parece emocionante porque es competitivo

8. Complete with the missing words
a. hacer b. parece c. Hago d. me / jugar e. jugué f. voy / es

9. Wordsearch

E		A	D	A	L	A	C	S	E	
T	A	B	U	R	R	I	D	O	J	
N	G						A			
A	O				N					
N	T		O		I				R	
O	A		M	T					A	
I	D		A	S					B	
C	O	M	P	E	T	I	T	I	V	O
O	R				L				R	
M						C			P	
E								I		
	O	M	S	I	R	U	T	L	U	C
A	R	R	I	E	S	G	A	D	O	

Bodybuilding: **Culturismo**
Cycling: **Ciclismo**
Skating: **Patinaje**
Climbing: **Escalada**
Exciting: **Emocionante**
Tiring: **Agotador**
Risky: **Arriesgado**
Competitive: **Competitivo**
To try: **Probar**
Boring: **Aburrido**

10. Translate into Spanish
a. Arriesgado b. Culturismo c. Voy a hacer d. Si pudiera e. Me gustaría probar
f. Emocionante g. Es competitivo h. El submarinismo

11. Gapped English to Spanish translation
a. escalada / parece emocionante b. culturismo / gimnasio / semana c. deporte / agotador
d. Juego / fútbol / domingos e. ciclismo / después f. probar / arriesgado g. vela / aburrida / horrible
h. parece / competitivo

12. Translate into Spanish
a. Hago culturismo en casa todos los días b. Me gusta el fútbol porque es emocionante
c. Juego al tenis tres veces a la semana d. No me gusta hacer natación porque es agotador
e. No me gusta hacer vela porque es aburrido f. Hago footing todos los sábados porque es relajante
g. Me gustaría probar el parapente porque es arriesgado

ANSWERS - Unit 11. Sport - Higher

1. Match

Hago ciclismo – *I do cycling*   Hice vela – *I did sailing*   Jugaré al baloncesto – *I will play basketball*
Hice ciclismo – *I did cycling*   Haré footing – *I will do jogging*   Haré vela – *I will do sailing*
Juego al baloncesto – *I play basketball*   Haré ciclismo – *I will do cycling*   Hago footing – *I do jogging*
Jugué al baloncesto – *I played basketball*   Hice culturismo – *I did bodybuilding*   Hice footing – *I did jogging*

2. Broken words

a. agot**ador**   b. arries**gado**   c. foot**ing**   d. est**adio**   e. pisc**ina**   f. bicicl**eta**   g. mañ**ana**   h. v**ela**
i. lug**ares**

3. Translate into English

a. *Entertaining* b. *Risky*   c. *Sailing*   d. *Once*   e. *If I could*   f. *To try*   g. *I will do*   h. *Tiring* i. *Paragliding*

4. Gapped translation

a. *I did/went*   b. *I will play*   c. *Tomorrow*   d. *I lost*   e. *I will*   f. *Try*   g. *I will go*   h. *I did*

5. Correct the wrong translation

a. El submarinismo: *Scuba diving*   b. El ciclismo: *Cycling/Bicycle*   c. √   d. El footing: *Jogging*
e. Jugaré: *I will play*   f. √   g. Sábado: *Saturday*   h. Probar: *To try*   i. Una vez: *Once*   j. Si pudiera: *If I could*

6. Break the flow

a. Lo hago en la piscina una vez a la semana   b. Si pudiera me gustaría probar el parapente
c. Ayer jugué al tenis con mi hermano y gané   d. El fin de semana que viene haré culturismo
e. Mis deportes favoritos son la escalada y el golf   f. Me gustaría probar el submarinismo
g. El submarinismo es un deporte fascinante   h. Normalmente entreno dos veces a la semana

7. Fill the gaps with the correct options

a. semana / ciclismo   b. jugué   c. pudiera / probar   d. demasiado   e. entreno / veces   f. general / hago

8. Wordsearch

										M	
		A	R	E	I	D	U	P	I	S	E
		A					R		G	E	
		B		H			E		U	T	
		O		A			F		S	N	
	É	R	A	G	U	J	I		T	A	
R		P		O			E		A	N	
A							R		R	I	
H							O		Í	C	
I		O	D	A	G	S	E	I	R	R	A	S
	C									A	
	E									F	

I will do: **Haré**
I will play: **Jugaré**
I did: **Hice**
To try: **Probar**
If I could: **Si pudiera**
I would like: **Me gustaría**
I do: **Hago**
I prefer: **Prefiero**
Fascinating: **Fascinante**

9. Tangled translation

a. entreno / veces   b. próximo / jugar   c. favorito / arriesgado   d. pudiera / me gustaría / submarinismo
e. deportes / equipo / competitivos   f. ayer / vela / genial   g. nunca / demasiado

10. Translate into English

a. *great*   b. *to try*   c. *risky*   d. *paragliding*   e. *team*   f. *bodybuilding*   g. *tiring*

11. Guided translation

a. Nunca juego   b. Si pudiera   c. Jugaré al fútbol   d. Es más competitivo   e. Es emocionante
f. Me gustaría probar   g. Entreno dos veces   h. Me parece divertido   i. Siempre gano

12. Translate into Spanish

a. Ayer, jugué al tenis y perdí   b. Mi deporte favorito es el atletismo. ¡Es divertido!
c. Me gustaría probar la escalada ya que es arriesgada   d. Nunca juego al golf porque me parece aburrido
e. Prefiero los deportes de equipo porque son más divertidos   f. Mañana voy a hacer culturismo con mi hermana
g. Por la mañana, normalmente hago footing solo   h. Una vez a la semana, juego al baloncesto en el colegio

THE LANGUAGE GYM

ANSWERS - UNIT 11 - Test (/100)

1. Vocabulary recognition: Spanish-to-English translation (/15)

a. A team sport	f. Yesterday	k. Great
b. Usually	g. From time to time	l. I did
c. Twice	h. The swimming pool	m. Scuba diving
d. Week	i. Fun	n. An/One hour
e. I always win	j. Climbing	o. To try

2. Syntax/Lexicogrammar – Split sentences (/5)

Entreno dos veces	**a la semana**
Prefiero los deportes	**de equipo**
No hago mucho	**deporte**
Ayer jugué	**al ping-pong**
La semana pasada	**hice vela**

3. Grammar/Morphology/Vocabulary – Tangled translation (/20)

a. Todos los **sábados**, hago **vela**

b. **Prefiero** los deportes **individuales**

c. **Entreno** dos veces a la **semana**

d. **Jugué** al ping pong y **fue** divertido

e. El fin de semana **pasado**, hice **boxeo**

f. **Ayer**, jugué al tenis y **gané**

g. Mañana **jugaré** al bádminton con mi **hermano**

h. En general, entreno **dos veces a la semana**

i. **Voy** a la **piscina** todos los domingos

j. **Mañana**, **haré** vela con mis amigos

k. **Mi** deporte **favorito** es la escalada

l. **Es un deporte** un poco **arriesgado**

4. Translate into Spanish (/ 60 – each full sentence – 6 points)

a. Me encantan los deportes de pelota como el fútbol y el baloncesto.

b. No soporto los deportes de equipo porque son aburridos.

c. Si pudiera, me gustaría probar la escalada.

d. Hago natación en la piscina cuatro veces por semana.

e. De vez en cuando hago culturismo. Lo hago en mi casa.

f. Me gustaría probar el parapente porque es arriesgado.

g. Voy al gimnasio y al estadio una vez por semana con mi hermana menor.

h. Un deporte que no me gusta nada es el footing. Es demasiado agotador.

i. Mañana, jugaré al tenis con mi hermano mayor.

j. Ayer hice vela con mi amigo, fue divertido.

 THE LANGUAGE GYM

Unit 12. Customs and festivals

KEY VOCABULARY Foundation

Las fiestas *(festivals)*

Cada año celebramos:

Each year, we celebrate

-el día de año nuevo: *New Year's Day*

-el día de la madre: *Mother's Day*

-el día del padre: *Father's Day*

-el día de los Reyes Magos: *Three Kings Day*

-el día de San Valentín: *Valentine's Day*

-el Eid al-Fitr: *Eid al-Fitr*

-la Navidad: *Christmas*

-la Pascua: *Easter*

Las religiones y lugares de culto

Los cristianos: *Christians*

Los hindúes: *Hindus*

Los judíos: *Jews*

Los musulmanes: *Muslims*

La iglesia: *The church*

La mezquita: *The mosque*

La sinagoga: *The synagogue*

El templo: *The temple*

Rezar a su Dios: *To pray to their God*

Expresiones de tiempo

Durante las fiestas religiosas:

During religious festivals

Cada año: *Each year*

Expresiones esenciales

La gente: *people*

-comparte comida: *share food*

-da regalos: *give gifts*

-está de vacaciones: *are on holidays*

-se reúne: *meet*

Es mi fiesta favorita porque:

It's my favourite festival because

-estoy de vacaciones: *I am on holidays*

-recibo regalos: *I receive gifts*

-veo a mi familia/mis amigos/mis primos:

I see my family/my friends/my cousins

Días festivos: *Public holidays*

Una comida festiva: *A festive meal*

Acontecimientos *(events)*

En la mayoría de las ciudades hay:

In most cities, there are

-conciertos: *concerts*

-desfiles: *processions*

-fuegos artificiales: *fireworks*

1. Match

La Pascua	*New year's day*
El día de los Reyes Magos	*During festivals*
El día de año nuevo	*Three Kings Day*
La Navidad	*People*
Los cristianos	*Easter*
Durante las fiestas	*People*
Los judíos	*Christmas*
Rezar a su Dios	*Jews*
La gente	*Gifts*
Los regalos	*To pray to their God*

2. Broken words

a. La igle_ _ _: *Church*

b. Di_ _: *God*

c. Reg_ _ _ _: *Gifts*

d. La mezqui_ _: *Mosque*

e. El día de a_ _ nuevo:
New Year's day

f. La Pas_ _ _: *Easter*

g. R_ _ _ _: *To pray*

h. Navid_ _: *Christmas*

3. Translate into English

a. El día de los Reyes Magos

b. Los cristianos

c. La gente

d. Año nuevo

e. El Eid al-Fitr

f. Yo recibo

g. El día de San Valentín

h. Navidad

4. Gapped translation

a. La gente da regalos: *People give _____*

b. Es mi fiesta favorita: *It's my favourite _____*

c. Voy a la iglesia: *I go to _____*

d. Veo a mi familia: *I _____ my family*

e. Celebramos Navidad: *We _____ Christmas*

f. Estoy de vacaciones: *I am on _____*

g. Recibo regalos: *I _____ gifts*

h. Una comida festiva: *A festive _____*

5. Correct the wrong translations

a. La gente: *Gifts*   f. Regalos: *Fireworks*

b. Los desfiles: *These files*   g. Fiesta: *Festival*

c. Veo: *I drink*   h. Iglesia: *Church*

d. Una comida: *A meal*   i. Conciertos: *Easter*

e. Pascua: *Easter*   j. Fuegos artificiales: *Fires*

6. Break the flow

a. Durantelasfiestaslagentesereúne

b. EnNavidadreciboregalos

c. Meencantanlascomidasfestivas

d. Eldíadeañonuevomegustaverlosfuegosartificiales

e. CelebrolaPascuaconmifamilia

f. Voyalamezquitaconmipadreymishermanos

g. CadaañocelebramoselDíadelosReyesMagos

h. Enmiciudadhaydesfilesyconciertos

7. Fill the gaps with the correct options

a. El día de año _____ hay fuegos artificiales

b. Mi_____ favorita es el día de la madre

c. En Pascua como _____ chocolate

d. En Navidad, recibo _____ de mis padres

e. Cada año _____ el Eid al-Fitr

f. En Navidad, las _____ se reúnen

familias	nuevo	mucho
regalos	celebramos	fiesta

8. Wordsearch – Find the Spanish for the listed words

A	C	V	M	U	A	T	I	U	Q	Z	E	M
R	E	R	E	I	L	A	T	A	N	D	P	R
T	L	E	I	R	B	L	A	N	E	A	L	O
I	E	Y	L	S	A	E	I	S	T	R	A	M
F	B	E	R	O	T	V	F	E	D	N	E	S
I	R	S	A	C	P	I	W	Y	L	A	R	A
C	A	M	D	I	L	H	A	M	A	R	C	V
I	M	A	N	E	S	Z	B	N	D	M	R	I
A	O	G	S	B	O	L	E	D	O	I	E	T
L	S	O	Ü	T	J	U	D	Í	O	S	H	S
E	R	S	E	I	N	B	R	J	E	N	O	E
S	A	M	D	B	C	O	M	I	D	A	S	F

Christians: Los _____

Jewish: Los _____

The Three Kings: Los _____ _____

Processions: Los d_____

Festive meals: Las _____ _____

Mosque: La _____

Fireworks: Los fuegos _____

We celebrate: _____

9. Tangled translation

a. Hay **processions** y algunos **concerts**

b. **We celebrate** la Navidad y la **Easter**

c. Mi fiesta **favourite** es el **Day** de **Saint Valentine**

d. Lo que más **I like are** los fuegos artificiales

e. El **New Year's Day** comemos **a lot**. ¡Me encantan las comidas **festive**!

f. Por Navidad **I receive** muchos **gifts**

g. En la **majority** de las **cities** hay conciertos

h. Por **Christmas**, las familias se **get together**

10. Translanagrams – Work out the hidden words and translate them into English

e.g. La Pauasc: La Pascua   *Easter*

a. oLs riscatison:

b. saL codamis fatiesvs:

c. soL esRey goMas:

d. Lso díjuos:

e. aL zumeqita:

f. oLs garelos de vaNidad:

g. Celamobers:

11. Guided translation

a. L__ P_____: *Easter*

b. El d__ de a__ n____: *New year's day*

c. La Navid__: *Christmas*

d. L__ j_____: *Jews*

e. L__ c_____ f_____: *Festive meals*

f. R_____ r_____: *I receive gifts*

g. H__ d_____: *There are processions*

12. Translate into Spanish

a. Every year, we celebrate Eid al-Fitr

b. I love Christmas because I receive gifts

c. Valentine's day is my favourite festival

d. I love festivals because there are fireworks

e. On New Year's Day the family gets together

f. In most cities there are processions

g. What I like the most are the festive meals

THE LANGUAGE GYM

KEY VOCABULARY Higher

1. Las fiestas
Cada año: *Each year*
El 25 de diciembre: *On the 25ᵗʰ December*
En casa: *At home*
Celebramos: *We celebrate*
-el día de año nuevo: *New Year's Day*
-el día de la madre / del padre
Mother's/Father's Day
-el día de los Reyes Magos: *Three Kings Day*
-el día de San Valentín: *Valentine's Day*
-los días festivos: *public holidays*

2. Adónde se va durante las fiestas religiosas
Durante las fiestas religiosas:
During religious festivals
Los cristianos: *Christians*
Los hindúes: *Hindus*
Los judíos: *Jews*
Los musulmanes: *Muslims*
van: *go*
-a la iglesia: *to the church*
-a la mezquita: *to the mosque*
-a la sinagoga: *to the synagogue*
-al templo: *to the temple*

3. Qué se hace durante las fiestas
La gente da regalos a sus:
People give gifts to their
-hijos / niños: *children*
-parientes: *relatives*
Los amigos / Las familias: *Friends / Families*
-se encuentran: *meet*
-se llaman: *call each other*
-se reúnen: *get together*
para: *in order to*
–cenar/celebrar/comer juntos/as:
dine/celebrate/eat together
En la mayoría de las ciudades hay:
In most cities there are
-desfiles: *processions*
-fuegos artificiales: *fireworks*

4. Mi fiesta favorita
Mi fiesta favorita es ... porque:
My favourite festival is ... because
-no voy al colegio: *I don't go to school*
-estoy de vacaciones: *I am on holidays*
-recibo regalos: *I receive gifts*
-veo a mis parientes/amigos/primos:
I see my relatives/friends/cousins

---

1. Match

En mi casa	*Gifts*
La Pascua	*New Year's day*
La fiesta	*People*
El día de año nuevo	*Christmas*
La Navidad	*Church*
Los musulmanes	*Christians*
La gente	*Each*
La iglesia	*At home*
Los cristianos	*Jews*
Cada	*Festival/Party*
Los niños	*Easter*
Los regalos	*Children*
Los parientes	*Relatives*

---

2. Gapped translation

a. Celebramos el día del padre: *We celebrate* _____

b. Van a la iglesia: *They go to the* _____

c. Los padres dan regalos: *Parents give* _____

d. Durante las fiestas: *During the* _____

e. Los amigos se encuentran: *Friends* _____

f. La gente se reúne: *People* _____

g. Celebrar juntos: *To celebrate* _____

h. Hay desfiles: *There are* _____

---

3. Translate into English

a. Los amigos se reúnen para cenar juntos.

b. La gente se encuentra con sus parientes.

c. Los musulmanes van a la mezquita.

d. En la mayoría de las ciudades hay desfiles.

e. Durante las fiestas veo a mis parientes.

f. No voy al colegio.

g. La gente da regalos.

---

4. Broken words

a. La N _ _ _ _ _ _
b. La igle _ _ _
c. Los desfi _ _ s
d. Mis pari _ _ _ _ _
e. Los fueg _ _ arti_icia_es
f. Los am _ _ _ _
g. Los reg_ _ _ _
h. La gen _ _

---

5. Missing vowels

a. M_zq_ _ t _ : *Mosque*
b. D_ sf_l_s: *Processions*
c. C_l_g_ _ : *School*
d. P_r_ _ nt_s: *Relatives*
e. _gl_s_ _ : *Church*
f. N_ñ_s: *Children*
g. P_sc_ _ : *Easter*

 **THE LANGUAGE GYM**

6. Choose the correct translation

a. Navidad: *Easter / Navigate / Christmas*

b. Pasar: *to spend / to rent / to buy*

c. Pascua: *Easter / Places / Pasta*

d. Celebrar: *to spend / to stay/ to celebrate*

e. Iglesia: *mosque / church / gift*

f. Regalos: *gifts / children / people*

7. Complete with the correct option from the box

a. Paso la Pascua con la _____

b. ___ 25 de diciembre es Navidad

c. A veces voy a la _____

d. La gente da _____

e. La gente se reúne y come _____

f. Mi _____ favorita es el día de año nuevo

junta
familia
fiesta
regalos
el
iglesia

8. Break the flow

a. Cadaañoel25dediciembrecelebramoslaNavidad

b. MifiestafavoritaesEidal-Fitr

c. Durantelasfiestasreligiosaslagentesereúne

d. Loscristianosvanalaiglesiaylosmusulmanesalamezquita

e. Lospadresdanregalosasusniños

f. Enlamayoríadelasciudadeshayconciertosydesfiles

g. Meencantanlosfuegosartificiales

h. LafiestadelosReyesMagosesenenero

9. Definition game

a. Una fiesta musulmana: E

b. Una fiesta cristiana: P

c. Lo que damos a los niños en Navidad: R

d. La fiesta del amor: S

e. El verbo de las fiestas: C

f. Un lugar de culto judío: S

g. Un lugar de culto cristiano: I

10. Complete the table

English	Español
	Días festivos
New Year's Day	
	Festivales religiosos
People give	
People meet	
	Veo
	Fuegos artificiales
In most cities	
	Cenar juntos

11. Translate into Spanish

a. *Children*: N

b. *Relatives*: P

c. *Together*: J

d. *Fireworks*: F

e. *Processions*: D

f. *Christians*: C

g. *At home*: E

h. *Public Holidays*: D

i. *Most*: La m

j. *To celebrate*: C

k. *To dine*: C

l. *To spend:* P

m. *Cities*: C

n. *Muslims*: M

o. *Gifts*: R

p. *Easter*: P

q. *Christmas*: N

r. *People*: G

12. Translate into Spanish

a. (The) Muslims go to the mosque and (the) Jews go to the synagogue:

b. During the festivals I see my relatives:

c. In most cities there are fireworks, processions and concerts:

d. On the 25th December we celebrate Christmas:

e. People meet and dine together:

f. My favourite festival is Easter because I eat chocolate eggs:

g. I receive gifts from my parents and grandparents:

h. I love Valentine's Day because I am romantic:

i. I love Christmas because I have long holidays:

1. Vocabulary recognition - Spanish-to-English translation (/15)

a. Los judíos	f. Sus	k. Recibo
b. Los cristianos	g. Las fiestas	l. Desfiles
c. Rezar	h. Regalos	m. Fuegos artificiales
d. Dios	i. Bueno	n. Veo
e. Parientes	j. Una comida	o. La gente

2. Syntax/Lexicogrammar – Split sentences (/5)

Estoy de	**el día del año nuevo**
La gente se reúne para	**vacaciones**
Me gusta ver	**pasar un buen rato junta**
Celebramos	**a sus parientes**
La gente da regalos	**los fuegos artificiales**

3. Grammar/Morphology/Vocabulary – Tangled translation (/20)

a. **We celebrate** el **day** de la madre

b. **During** las fiestas **religious**

c. La **people** da **gifts** a sus parientes

d. **We go** a la **church**

e. **I don't go** al **school**

f. **Usually**, son días **festive (holidays)**

g. La gente se **meet** con sus **friends** y **relatives**

h. La gente **spend** un buen **moment** junta

i. In most **ciudades** hay **processions**

j. Mi fiesta **favourite** son las **Easter**

k. Hay **fireworks** y **concerts**

l. En **Christmas**, normalmente veo a mis **uncles**

4. Translate into Spanish (/ 60 – each full sentence – 6 points)

a. At Christmas, parents give gifts to their children.

b. The whole family gets together to dine and celebrate together.

c. On 6th January, (the) Christians celebrate the Three Kings Day.

d. During most religious festivals we don't go to school.

e. My favourite festival is Eid al-Fitr because I see my cousins.

f. In all cities there are processions, concerts and fireworks.

g. During Easter (the) Jews go to the synagogue to pray to their God.

h. I love Valentine's Day because my boyfriend gives me a gift.

i. We get together at my house to have a good time.

j. My favourite festival is Easter because I eat chocolate eggs.

THE LANGUAGE GYM

ANSWERS - Unit 12. Customs and festivals - Foundation

1. Match

La Pascua – *Easter*   El día de los Reyes Magos – *Three Kings Day*
El día de año nuevo – *New Year's Day*   La Navidad – *Christmas*   Los cristianos – *Christians*
Durante las fiestas – *During festivals*   Los judíos – *Jews*   Rezar a su Dios – *To pray to their God*
La gente – *People*   Los regalos – *Gifts*

2. Broken words

a. La igle**sia** b. Di**os** c. Reg**alos** d. La mezqu**ita** e. El día de a**ño** nuevo f. La Pas**cua** g. **Rezar** h. Navid**ad**

3. Translate into English

a. *Three Kings Day* b. *Christians* c. *People* d. *New Year's Day* e. *Eid al-Fitr* f. *I receive*
g. *Valentine's Day* i. *Christmas*

4. Gapped translation

a. *People give **gifts*** b. *It's my favourite **festival*** c. *I go to **church*** d. *I **see** my family*
e. *We **celebrate** Christmas* f. *I am on **holidays*** g. *I **receive** gifts* h. *A festive **meal***

5. Correct the wrong translation

a. La gente: *People* b. Los desfiles: *Processions* c. Veo: *I see* d. √ e. Regalos: *Gifts* f. √ g. √ h.
Conciertos: *Concerts* i. √ j. Fuegos artificiales: *Fireworks*

6. Break the flow

a. Durante las fiestas la gente se reúne b. En Navidad recibo regalos c. Me encantan las comidas festivas
d. El día de año nuevo me gusta ver los fuegos artificiales e. Celebro la Pascua con mi familia
f. Voy a la mezquita con mi padre y mis hermanos g. Cada año celebramos el Día de los Reyes Magos
h. En mi ciudad hay desfiles y conciertos

7. Fill the gaps with the correct options

a. nuevo b. fiesta c. mucho d. regalos e. celebramos f. familias

8. Wordsearch

A	C				A	T	I	U	Q	Z	E	M
R	E	R							D			
T	L	E	I					E				
I	E	Y		S			S					
F	B	E			T		F					S
I	R	S				I						A
C	A	M			L		A					V
I	M	A		E			N					I
A	O	G	S						O			T
L	S	O			J	U	D	Í	O	S		S
E		S										E
S				C	O	M	I	D	A	S		F

Christians: Los **cristianos**
The Jews: Los **judíos**
The Three Kings: Los **Reyes Magos**
Processions: Los **desfiles**
Festive meals: Las **comidas festivas**
Mosque: La **mezquita**
Fireworks: Los fuegos **artificiales**
We celebrate: **Celebramos**

9. Tangled translation

a. desfiles / conciertos b. Celebramos / Pascua c. favorita / Día / San Valentín d. me gusta son
e. El día de Año Nuevo / mucho / festivas f. recibo / regalos g. mayoría / ciudades h. Navidad / reúnen

10. Translanagrams – Work out the hidden words and translate them into English

a. la pauasc: La Pascua *Easter* b. Los cristianos: *Christians* c. Las comidas festivas: *A festive meal*
d. Los Reyes Magos: *The Three Kings* e. Los judíos: *Jews* f. La mezquita: *The mosque*
g. Los regalos de Navidad: *Christmas gifts* h. Celebramos: *We celebrate*

11. Guided translation

a. La Pascua b. El día de año nuevo c. La Navidad d. Los judíos e. Las comidas festivas
f. Recibo regalos g. Hay desfiles

12. Translate into Spanish

a. Cada año celebramos Eid al-Fitr b. Me encanta la Navidad porque recibo regalos
c. El día de San Valentín es mi fiesta favorita d. Me encantan los festivales porque hay fuegos artificiales
e. En el día de Año Nuevo las familias se reúnen f. En la mayoría de las ciudades hay desfiles
g. Lo que más me gusta son las comidas festivas

THE LANGUAGE GYM

ANSWERS - Unit 12. Customs and festivals - Higher

1. Match
En mi casa – *At home*   La Pascua – *Easter*   La fiesta – *Festival/Party*
El día de año nuevo – *New Year's Day*   La Navidad – *Christmas*   Los musulmanes – *Muslims*
La gente – *People*   La iglesia – *Church*   Los cristianos – *Christians*   Cada – *Each*
Los niños – *Children*   Los regalos – *Gifts*   Los parientes – *Relatives*

2. Gapped translation
a. Father's Day   b. church   c. presents   d. festivals/parties   e. meet   f. get together   g. together
h. processions

3. Translate into English
a. Friends meet to dine together   b. People get together with their relatives   c. Muslims go to the mosque
d. In most cities there are processions   e. During festivals I see my relatives   f. I don't go to school
g. People offer gifts

4. Broken words
a. La **N**avi**d**ad   b. La igle**sia**   c. Los des**fi**les   d. Mis pari**entes**   e. Los fueg**os** artificiales   f. Los am**igos**
g. Los reg**alos**   h. La gen**te**

5. Missing vowels
a. mezquita   b. desfiles   c. colegio   d. parientes   e. iglesia   f. niños   g. Pascua

6. Choose the correct translation
a. Navidad: *Christmas*   b. Pasar: *to spend*   c. Pascua: *Easter*   d. Celebrar: *to celebrate*   e. Iglesia: *church*
f. Regalos: *gifts*

7. Complete with the correct option from the box
a. familia   b. El   c. iglesia   d. regalos   e. junta   f. fiesta

8. Break the flow
a. Cada año el 25 de diciembre celebramos la Navidad   b. Mi fiesta favorita es Eid al-Fitr
c. Durante las fiestas religiosas la gente se reúne
d. Los cristianos van a la iglesia y los musulmanes a la mezquita   e. Los padres dan regalos a sus niños
f. En la mayoría de las ciudades hay conciertos y desfiles   g. Me encantan los fuegos artificiales
h. La fiesta de los Reyes Magos es en enero

9. Definition game
a. Eid al-Fitr   b. Pascua   c. Regalos   d. San Valentín   e. Celebrar   f. Sinagoga   g. Iglesia

10. Complete the table
Public holidays: **Días festivos**   *New Year's Day:* **El día de Año Nuevo**
Religious festivals: **Festivales religiosos**   *People give:* **La gente da**   *People meet:* **La gente se reúne**
I see: **Veo**   *Fireworks:* **Fuegos artificiales**   *In most cities:* **En la mayoría de las ciudades**
To dine together: **Cenar juntos**

11. Translate into Spanish
a. Niños   b. Parientes   c. Juntos   d. Fuegos artificiales   e. Desfiles   f. Cristianos   g. En mi casa
h. Días festivos   i. La mayoría   j. Celebrar   k. Cenar   l. Pasar   m. Ciudades   n. Musulmanes   o. Regalos
p. Pascua   q. Navidad   r. Gente

12. Translate into Spanish
a. Los musulmanes van a la mezquita y los judíos a la sinagoga
b. Durante las fiestas veo a mis parientes
c. En la mayoría de ciudades hay fuegos artificiales, desfiles y conciertos
d. El 25 de diciembre celebramos la Navidad
e. La gente se reúne y cena junta
f. Mi fiesta favorita es la Pascua porque como huevos de chocolate
g. Recibo regalos de mis padres y mis abuelos
h. Me encanta el día de San Valentín porque soy romántico/a
i. Me encanta la Navidad porque tengo vacaciones largas

 THE LANGUAGE GYM

ANSWERS - UNIT 12 - Test (/100)

1. Vocabulary recognition: Spanish to English translation (/15)

a. Jews

b. Christians

c. To pray

d. God

e. Relatives

f. Their

g. Festivals

h. Gifts/Presents

i. Good

j. A meal

k. I receive

l. Processions

m. Fireworks

n. I see

o. People

2. Syntax/Lexicogrammar – Split sentences (/5)

Estoy de	**vacaciones**
La gente se reúne para	**pasar un buen rato junta**
Me gusta ver	**los fuegos artificiales**
Celebramos	**el día de año nuevo**
La gente da regalos	**a sus parientes**

3. Grammar/Morphology/Vocabulary – Tangled translation (/20)

a. **Celebramos** el **día** de la madre

b. **Durante** las fiestas **religiosas**

c. La **gente** da **regalos** a sus parientes

d. **Vamos** a la **iglesia**

e. **No voy** al **colegio**

f. **Normalmente**, son días **festivos**

g. La gente se **reúne** con sus **amigos** y **parientes**

h. La gente **pasa** un buen **rato** junta

i. En la mayoría de **ciudades**, hay **desfiles**

j. Mi fiesta **preferida/favorita** es la **Pascua**

k. Hay **fuegos artificiales** y **conciertos**

l. En **Navidad**, normalmente veo a mis **tíos**

4. Translate into Spanish (/ 60 – each full sentence – 6 points)

a. En Navidad, los padres dan regalos a sus hijos.

b. La familia se reúne para cenar y celebrar juntos.

c. El seis de enero los cristianos celebran el día de los Reyes Magos.

d. Durante la mayoría de fiestas religiosas no vamos al colegio.

e. Mi festival preferido/favorito es Eid al-Fitr porque veo a mis primos.

f. En la mayoría de ciudades hay desfiles, conciertos y fuegos artificiales.

g. Durante la Pascua, los judíos van a la sinagoga para rezar a su Dios.

h. Me encanta San Valentín porque mi novio me da un regalo.

i. Nos reunimos en mi casa para pasar un buen rato.

j. Mi fiesta favorita es la Pascua porque como huevos de chocolate.

THE LANGUAGE GYM

Printed in Great Britain
by Amazon

24806091R00057